"I echo the sentiments of Charlie 'Tremendous' Jones, who wisely said, 'You'll be the same person five years from now that you are today, with the exception of the books you read, the recordings you hear, and the people with whom you associate.' And if that holds true—buy and read *Streetwise to Saleswise* immediately and apply the lessons in your career. With its engaging storyline, lovable characters, and timeless message, Jeff West and Bob Burg have crafted a sales parable poised to become a classic."

~Andy Glaub, Senior Vice-President & Director of Sales, Aflac U.S.

"Few books carry the equal attributes of 'fun' and 'instructive' but *Streetwise to Saleswise* checks both of those boxes. Read this book with a pen in your hand and jot down all the nuggets along the way. We all have some Thaddeus in us, and we all need an Andre in our lives. Read for the entertainment, but apply for the surge in sales!"

~Jeff Shore, author of *Follow-Up and Close the Sale*

"*Streetwise to Saleswise: Become Objection Proof*™ *and Beat the Sales Blues* is the affirmation that we all encounter similar experiences in sales and service-related roles. Perceived objections and potential rejections are not exclusive, and should not be internalized, but leverage as learning moments or greater understanding. West and Burg encourage us to listen, learn, and push forward to take the high road. Success will result! And as someone with deep ties to New Orleans, this is truly the *lagniappe* bonus gift of all sales books that will resonate!"

~DeAnn B. Golden, President and CEO, Berkshire Hathaway HomeServices Georgia Properties

"*Streetwise to Saleswise* is an exceptional sales book that takes you through the sales process in a very enjoyable story. That isn't easy to find! On top of that, it gives usable nuggets to implement in sales strategies. It may even challenge some beliefs you had about sales in a very positive way. I will be purchasing this book for my sales team."

~Heath Oakes, CEO, National Family Care Life Insurance Company

"Being compelled to finish a non-fiction book in one sitting is rare; doing so while learning new sales lessons after 30-plus years of selling is priceless. *Streetwise to Saleswise* gets a special place on my shelf as one of my new go-to recommendations and favorites for those new to selling and those who want to be the best in the world at helping their clients."

~April Shprintz, leading sales expert and award-winning author of *Magic Blue Rocks, The Secret to Doing Anything.*

"When was the last time you read a book about sales that had drama, likable characters, lessons in success, and even a little romance? How about never! *Streetwise to Saleswise* is a great blend of story and lessons in sales and in life. And the concept of becoming Objection-Proof™ is brilliant! I won't tell you if the guy gets the girl. You'll have to read the book yourself, all the way to the end."

~Bill Cates, CSP, CPAE
author of *Beyond Referrals* and *Radical Relevance*

"I love this book! Congratulations to Jeff West and Bob Burg for writing one the most creative and innovative sales books on the market today. *Streetwise to Saleswise* captures your attention from the very first chapter, and immediately pulls you in with engaging characters and a beautifully written story, packed full of original and powerful ideas designed to increase your sales performance. It is rare that in today's marketplace you find a book that is both so incredibly useful and so fun to read!"

~Meridith Elliott Powell, business growth strategist and Hall of Fame speaker, award-winning author of *THRIVE: Turn Uncertainty To Competitive Advantage*

"*Streetwise to Saleswise* is a goldmine of practical tips, deep insights, and effective tools to elevate your sales skills and success. If you're ALL IN, when it comes to succeeding in your sales career, read this book! Written as a parable in the style of *The Go-Giver*, you'll find this book transformative and powerful-filled with simple yet profound strategies to strip away the unnecessary stress and suffering sometimes associated with selling, and replacing it with a true sense of service, satisfaction, and achievement. The strategies in this book have brought about remarkable changes for Jeff's and Bob's clients in the corporate world, enhancing the performance of sales and leadership teams, executives, and entrepreneurs."

~ Chris Dorris, *The* Mental Toughness Coach

"Thaddeus Tucker's journey from losing his job to conquering sales is heartwarming and relatable. The authors have expertly weaved a story that could easily stand by itself, even if we weren't being taught the lessons he learned. But we were! You get pulled into the story and root for Thaddeus. You don't even realize until the end that you have learned things that will help you with your life and career. As a top direct sales leader, I believe everyone would benefit from *Streetwise to Saleswise!*"

~Lisa M. Wilber, coauthor of the award-winning book *Said the Lady with the Blue Hair*

"I emerged from the pages armed with a fresh perspective to integrate into my sales approach and a renewed vision for forging meaningful connections with potential clients. The delightful storytelling, coupled with the immersive journey of our main character, had me hooked from the very beginning, experiencing every high and low alongside him."

~Grant Muller, speaker, coach, and author of *Top of Heart*

"For our personal health and well being, prevention is ALWAYS better than cure. The same is true for the obstacles that appear in the sales process, and this beautifully crafted story in *Streetwise to Saleswise* shares the meal plan and habits required to keep you out of sales surgery, and instead achieving positive outcomes for everyone involved"

~Phil M Jones, creator of *Exactly What to Say*

"It's rare that a parable successfully integrates the business principles the book is intended to deliver with a genuinely entertaining story. What's more rare, is for the story itself to carry as many life lessons as business concepts. But that's exactly what happens in *Streetwise to Saleswise* authored by Jeff West and Bob Burg. These two sales authorities, who are also award-winning authors, combine their experience and wisdom in a manner that is easy to understand. What's more important, is that the sales concepts the book delivers have been proven successful over decades."

~Bill Ellis, Brand Architect and author of *Women Who Won*

"The authors of *Streetwise to Saleswise* have crafted a charming story in which you'll be instantly transported to New Orleans and into the lives of Thaddeus, a new but open-minded salesperson, and his manager, Andre. Lessons are woven into each scene and you'll find gems on sales (including step by step tactics), leadership, and serving others. By the end you'll be more effective and probably be ready for a trip to 'The Big Easy'."

~Andrea Waltz, co-author of *Go for No!*

"This delightful story engaged me from start to finish. I was immediately taken by Thad's story and the kaleidoscope of characters he encounters on his journey. The vibrant sights and sounds of New Orleans painted a colorful picture, making the sales lessons infinitely indelible. Jeff West and Bob Burg are maestros of storytelling who manage to weave educational content into the narrative so seamlessly that learning feels like an adventure. Prepare to be inspired, entertained, and educated all at once. You will never approach sales the same way again once you learn the magic of Fusion Points™ and how to effectively build to a close and clinch it with creativity and confidence."

~Alexandra Watkins
Founder, Eat My Words, author of *Hello, My Name Is Awesome*

"*Streetwise to Saleswise* is a gem of a book, a beautiful story that will warm your heart while teaching you timeless principles of authentically human salesmanship. Essential reading for everyone on your team!"

~John David Mann, coauthor of *The Go-Giver, The Latte Factor,* and *The Slight Edge*

"Jeff West and Bob Burg have written the next sales classic! Their parable pulled me in from the first page and was so engaging, I didn't want it to end. They masterfully weaved their sales lessons into the story in a way that made them forever fused into my heart and mind. It felt effortless to read and learn."

~Kathy Tagenel, President, Go-Givers International

"A delightfully entertaining story that will touch your heart while also helping you to navigate the trials and tribulations of life in sales. I love that the authors combined music, entertainment, leadership and sales, it makes for a short fun read that leaves you smarter and more inspired."

~Lisa Earle McLeod, bestselling author of
Selling with Noble Purpose

"I've read hundreds of sales books, and *Streetwise to Saleswise* is the first one to cause me to be transported into a mind-movie where I was LIVING the experiences along with Thaddeus, Andre, and Livia, while also seeing and hearing sales lessons being taught and practiced. Jeff West and Bob Burg have combined their captivating storytelling and expert sales training skills to create a highly entertaining and educational book that will benefit not only those with 'sales' in their title, but anyone who wants to be better at communicating with others."

~Art Sobczak, author of *Smart Calling-Eliminate the Fear, Failure, and Rejection from Cold Calling*

Also by the Authors

Authored by Bob Burg

Endless Referrals: Network Your Everyday Contacts Into Sales
Adversaries Into Allies: Master the Art of Ultimate Influence

Co-authored with John David Mann

The Go-Giver: A Little Story About a Powerful Business Idea
Go-Givers Sell More
The Go-Giver Leader: A Little Story About What Matters Most in Business
The Go-Giver Influencer: A Little Story About a Most Persuasive Idea

Authored by Jeff C. West

The Unexpected Tour Guide
Fusion Points™ Engage the Science of Persistence
The 7.5 Essential Selling Skills
Survival Skills for Commission Salespeople in Insurance

Co-authored with Lisa M. Wilber

Said the Lady With the Blue Hair: 7 Rules for Success in Direct Sales Wrapped in a Wonderful Lesson for Life

Streetwise to Saleswise

Become ObjectionProof™ and Beat the Sales Blues

Streetwise to Saleswise

Become ObjectionProof™ and Beat the Sales Blues

by

Jeff C. West and Bob Burg

Published by

West Marketing Group, Inc.

PO Box 752

Giddings, TX 78942

www.jeffcwest.com

Library of Congress Control Number: 2023918268

ISBN: (Paperback) 978-0-9973614-7-6

ISBN:(Hardback I.S.) 979-8-9892229-1-9

eISBN: (eReader) 978-0-9973614-8-3

ISBN: (Downloadable Audio File) 978-0-9973614-9-0

Edited by Jessi Akins

Table of Contents

A Free Gift For You

Bob and Jeff would like to share a free 3-part video series with you based on the principles found in *Streetwise to Saleswise.*

How to Master the Art of Becoming ObjectionProof™

To get your free gift, please go to
https://jeffcwest.com/videos/

Or scan this QR Code.

Receive Bob's Daily Impact Emails

Enjoy a dose of morning inspiration to power up your day, including thoughts on sales, leadership, communication, and more!

You can view a sample issue and, if you'd like, subscribe at:

http://burg.com/daily-impact

Dedication

To my Dad (*z"l*) and Mom. Absolutely "no objections" to the greatest parents a son could have ever been blessed with.

~ Bob

To Lindsay and Whitney—being your dad has been, and always will be, my greatest joy in life. And to John David Mann, my favorite author, my mentor, and my friend.

~Jeff

Preface

H *e stood on the front porch of his dilapidated mobile home. His eyes filled with tears and a chilly rain made a gentle patter on the tin roof above his head.*
He refused to go back inside.
The reason?
Minutes earlier, he'd just broken the news to his young daughters, the most cherished souls he knew, that someone had mistakenly given their bicycles away to a local charity—and he couldn't afford to re-place them. Resilient as the girls were, they were no longer crying. They had gone back to playing inside the home. As for him, his tears refused to stop...

As I read those initial paragraphs, they seem more like the opening scene of a movie, rather than the introduction to a business parable.

But it isn't a scene from a movie.

It's a scene from my life.

The heartbroken man who felt he'd totally let his family down was me.

I had quit my job and begun a commission-only sales position for an insurance company—my only qualification being I'd successfully sold before in other industries. But those sales positions came with a salary, or draw against commissions. Now I was swinging from the trapeze of a sales career with no net below. No sales equaled no income.

Add to that, between the time of my prior sales success and this new beginning, I endured an eighteen-month period that could only be described as a dismal failure.

I was going under financially.

I moved my wife and two daughters out of a nice middle-class neighborhood into a "trailer house," as we used to say back in Georgia, which was in horrible condition. The floor was falling through in several places, and the gas range seemed almost dangerous.

An attorney advised me to declare bankruptcy.

I refused.

Why, you ask?

First, I was responsible for the debts I owed. I had every intent of paying my creditors back—which (spoiler alert) I eventually did. And second, the attorney wanted $1,200 to file the paperwork.

I didn't have $1,200.

Yes, I may be the first person in history to have been too broke to file bankruptcy.

I was struggling to make sales in my new business. I was struggling to feed my family. I was struggling to even survive.

That would be a really sad story, if it were the end. However, it wasn't the end... it was the beginning.

Within two years, I had gotten back on my feet and moved my family out of that place. Within four years, I had repaired my credit enough that we bought a brand new 3,400 square foot house, and I was earning a six-figure income.

Although I was finally regaining my financial footing, my career was still missing a beat until three years later.

In January of the year 2000, a mentor and sales manager of mine, Frank Davies, gave me two books that skyrocketed my career. The first was *The 21 Irrefutable Laws of Leadership,* by Dr. John C. Maxwell. And the second was *Endless Referrals,* by my coauthor, Bob Burg.

Without hesitation or apology, I say those two books changed the trajectory of my career. More important—they changed the future of my family.

It's not that those two books taught me how to become a more effective insurance salesperson and leader. Although every morsel in them certainly made me better at both. But the manuscripts had absolutely nothing to do with my industry.

Instead, I made the decision to learn the concepts and adapt them to my business. When I did so, I became more successful. I began to win... and win consistently.

If you are a professional entrepreneur, leader, or salesperson, Bob and I encourage... no, we *challenge* you to do the same with *Streetwise to Saleswise*.

Regardless of your industry, this book can help you. Hopefully, it will be as life changing for you as those books were for me.

If you're struggling, you can change that when you apply what you'll learn. If you're already successful, you can elevate your success and find it easier to sustain. More importantly, you'll learn how to lead others in achieving their success as well. I hope you'll take that responsibility as your calling.

Wishing you the best of success!

~Jeff C. West

Prologue

Well, *that's just great, Thaddeus Tucker! What are you gonna do now?*

Thaddeus sat on the bench overlooking the waterway in New Orleans' Louis Armstrong Park. What *was* he going to do?

He gazed up at the arched bridge of exposed steel and weathered wood that spanned the lush lagoon and fountains. To his right, the Mahalia Jackson Theater for the Performing Arts; to the left, the towering statue of the great Louis Armstrong. Satchmo: the master of scat. King of improvisation.

Thaddeus sighed. If only he could improvise like Satchmo. Maybe this day would have ended more like a jazz classic.

Instead, it ended like a semi-truck full of pianos in a head-on collision with a busload of tubas, mangled brass and whipping strings scattered everywhere along the freeway.

And to make matters worse... it was him that caused the crash.

Those words taunted his memories again.

Well, that's just great, Thaddeus Tucker! What are you gonna do now?

Were those his own thoughts? Or was he recalling his mother's words from his misspent youth?

Maybe both.

She always used his full name when she was scolding him for inappropriate behavior, which happened pretty often back in his teenage years. 'Course, you'd expect a certain amount of that from any young man who spent as many hours on the streets of New Orleans as he did. But Thaddeus seemed to excel at making borderline bad choices.

1

Inappropriate behavior? Indeed.

Trouble? No doubt.

At least he had a gift for avoiding anything that would cause harm to himself or others. He stayed just out of reach of the long arm of the law… and from the even longer arms of his mama.

Streetwise.

That's how Thaddeus explained it to his mother.

"I'm streetwise, Jolie. Just havin' fun with my friends. We ain't doin' nothin' bad. I know where to draw the line."

"*Streetwise?* You aren't even streetwise enough to know better than to call me Jolie! *Wise-mouthed* is more like it."

She'd put her hands on her hips and leaned forward for emphasis. "You can call me 'Mother.' You can call me 'Mama.' Better yet, you can just call me 'Ma'am.' But if you call me Jolie one more time, the only thing you'll be puttin' into your mouth for dinner tonight will be a bar of soap!"

She turned around and headed into the kitchen. "Don't you *ever* call me 'Jolie' again," she muttered.

Being streetwise, and knowing that his mama was making fresh-baked bread along with a rich potato stew for dinner (his two favorite dishes in her repertoire), he wisely chose hunger over valor and said, "Yes, ma'am."

Thaddeus had been trying to get his mother to call him Thad instead of Thaddeus, which to him sounded like an old geezer's name. He smiled now as he thought back on how miserably he had failed in that effort.

His friends called him Thad. So did his teachers.

But not his mother.

Attempting to budge her insistence on using his full name, Thaddeus had gotten the bright idea that every time she did so, he would refer to her by her given name as well.

"Thaddeus, would you please set the table?"

"Yes, Jolie."

"*What* did you call me?"

"'Jolie.' That *is* your name, right?"

"Yes, but why are *you* using it?"

"I'm almost a man now, Jolie. And I want to be called 'Thad,' not 'Thaddeus.' I've asked you to do that a hundred times. But since you won't, I thought I'd start calling you 'Jolie.'"

He delivered those words with a significant amount of pride in how grown-up he'd felt. *Almost a man.* That was his favorite part.

His pride, along with his *almost* manhood, shriveled like a leaking balloon as he saw the look on his mother's face.

She spoke slowly, emphasizing each word, a sure sign that his mouth had taken him one step beyond safety.

"I did *not* name you Thad."

Her pace quickened. "And what's a *Thad,* anyway? I named you Thaddeus, which means *courageous heart.* That was my grand-daddy's name. That's your name. And that's the name you *will* be called, young man."

"Well, it's a good thing it means courageous heart." he replied.

"Why's that?"

"I'd better be courageous, 'cause with a name like Thaddeus in this neighborhood, I'm gonna get beat up a lot!"

She remained annoyed—but also stifled a laugh.

~~~

A magical sound coming from his left interrupted Thaddeus's memories.

A nearby Dixieland band struck up one of his favorite tunes, "Muskrat Ramble", a tune first recorded in 1926 by none other than Louis Armstrong himself. Starting at Satchmo's feet, the band marched toward the bench where Thaddeus sat.

Marched?

More like sauntered.

Actually, *ramble* put it perfectly.

When Dixieland bands move, it looks less like a military formation, and more like friends out on a stroll. They *rambled* toward Thaddeus.

Thaddeus looked up at the statue again.

Mama's been gone for a while now, Satch. It's up to you. What do you think I should do?

Thaddeus had a good heart. He was a relatively bright man and could learn most anything he set his mind to. Hard work was no challenge for him. He was kind, energetic, and had a great—although often ill-timed—sense of humor.

In so many ways, he was the type of man anyone would enjoy calling a friend.

The one exception? His mouth.

Sure, his driver's license said he was thirty-three. But the words from his lips were often more akin to those of a smart-aleck teenager who needed to be grounded. Inappropriate comments landed Thaddeus in trouble more than once.

He leaned back on the park bench and closed his eyes. A slow, deep breath filled his lungs. His heart, on the other hand, was filled with the sounds of the music and thoughts of his mother.

Mom, I wish you were still here.

1

The Cause of the Crash

T hat morning had started off pretty much like every other August morning in the Big Easy, a nickname that perfectly reflected the music, the cuisine, and the local culture.

Thaddeus awoke at 6:30 a.m., when the timer on his programmable coffee-maker clicked on, and the machine began to make a *Darth Vader*-like noise.

Hissing.

Gurgling.

It almost seemed to say, *"Thaddeus... hiss... hiss... I am your coffee."*

Thaddeus watched as the carafe finished filling with his morning brew, an aromatic blend of his own creation. Coffee with chicory, cinnamon, and just a pinch of cayenne pepper.

He poured a cup and slowly inhaled. The aroma traveled deep into his lungs and comforted his mind.

He smiled and took a sip.

Many of Thaddeus's friends liked cinnamon in their coffee. Some liked chicory. But almost no one wanted cayenne pepper.

When he and his friends would meet at a coffee shop, Thaddeus would bring a small jar of organic cayenne pepper. He would offer the spice to his friends. Most would decline. Although a few would give in after Thaddeus's repeated insistence that they expand their horizons.

For whatever reason, Thaddeus felt completely at ease telling everyone how they should drink their coffee.

How to do their jobs.

How to run their businesses.

And how to best enjoy the city.

He wasn't bossy. At least he didn't think so. He just knew how things should be done and didn't mind imparting his knowledge to those within earshot.

Fortunately, he had learned at a very young age to use humor when this particular habit got him into uncomfortable situations. But *unfor-*tunately, according to his friends, that humor was often sarcastic and made things worse.

Sarcastic? Me? I'm not sarcastic! I'm funny!

Thaddeus walked out onto his small back patio, eased down into the chair, and absorbed the sights, scents, and sounds that gave New Orleans its distinctive character. It was a warm and humid morning. Condensate was dripping off his patio furniture.

"Ahh. New Orleans, Louisiana. Home of the *air* you can *wear,*" he said with a sigh. He loved his city, except for the hot and humid summers.

He drank his coffee, scrolling through the sports and local news on his smartphone. He browsed the headlines and when something piqued his interest, he would click to learn more.

This morning, one particular headline caused his thumb to stop quickly.

Local Company, Stiller Incorporated, Acquired by Stencil, Osgood, and Broughton, LTD.

Hoping that the headline was a click-bait lie, he followed the link to read the article.

It was not click-bait.

Local employee benefit-services company Stiller Incorporated, to be acquired by the nationwide insurance brokerage company, Stencil, Osgood and Broughton, LTD. Terms of the deal have not been re-

leased. Local customers and employees likely to be absorbed into their existing operations.

He didn't read any further. He slid his phone onto the table and took another sip of coffee.

Thaddeus started at Stiller ten years earlier in an entry-level position. Over that time, he'd earned promotions consistently, impressed the owner on many occasions, and was now the head of customer service for the company.

Well, that stinks! I've really enjoyed working at Stiller.

His mind raced through several possibilities. Would he be laid off?

His stomach churned. Could've been the chicory in his coffee. Could've been the cayenne pepper. Or it could have been the fear that came from knowing that his future was about to make an unexpected course change.

He went inside, took a long shower, and got dressed for the day.

On his drive in to work, the local radio station talk show was discussing the acquisition as well.

"This will be great for New Orleans!" said one host. "The company will be stronger, and jobs will be more secure."

"I don't agree!" said the other voice. "This is just another example of big companies swallowing smaller companies. The employees and customers will all suffer."

Thaddeus turned the radio off.

If I wanted to listen to people argue over things that already make me uneasy, I'd turn on the national news and get the latest political commentaries.

Arriving at the office, he noticed a few of his work friends hanging around outside. The nervous group was almost whispering, as he joined them.

Marcel, one of the floor managers, said, "Did you hear the news, brotha? Dey've done sold us out."

"Read about it this morning," replied Thaddeus.

"Well, I ga-ron-tee dat dis ain't gonna go so pretty well. We're all in a beaucoup o' trouble when dis shakes out. I may give ol' Cooter Brown a run for his money tonight!"

Ellen, who hadn't lived in New Orleans for very long and still struggled with the local dialect—especially Marcel's thick *Cajun* accent, asked, "Uh… wha… what was that?"

Antoinette replied, "That fool thinks—no, that fool *guarantees* we'll be in a lot of trouble when the details come out. And he plans to have a few drinks tonight."

Marcel said, "More than a few!"

Ellen raised an eyebrow and asked, *"Ol' Cooter Brown?"*

Thaddeus replied, "That's a saying around here if somebody plans to really tie one on. They're gonna get drunker than *ol' Cooter Brown.*"

Ellen said, "Well, a lot of sayings around here are new to me, but I've never heard that one! Where'd that originate?"

Looking around at each other, no one had the answer. Finally, Marcel spoke up and said, "Sha, it don't matter. It just *is.*"

Ellen asked Thaddeus, "Why did he call me shy?"

Thaddeus laughed and replied, "Not *Shy.* It's *Sha.* It's a term of endearment. No worries."

"Well, we'd all be better off not expecting the worst as we go in there this morning," Ellen said. "Maybe it'll work out for the best. It could mean that we get a lot more work."

Thaddeus said, "That's right, Marcel. You may get busier than a one-legged man in an ass-kickin' contest!"

They all laughed. It was a nervous laugh, but it seemed to brighten their mood, at least a little.

As they walked inside, Philip, a coworker from the shipping department, was standing there to greet them.

Philip was famous for two things: singing at the top of his lungs so that he could be heard over the general office chatter, and his absolutely *horrible* voice.

Philip held up a sign he'd made.

8

It said, "Will stop singing for five dollars or two beignets."

Everyone laughed again.

Philip said, "I'm just gettin' ready for life on the street. I've already picked out my corner near the Cafe du Monde."

"If you're standing there singing, people will pay a *lot* of money to get you to stop. Brilliant marketing!" laughed Thaddeus.

Philip tapped the side of the head with his index finger and winked. "Always thinking!"

A notice posted in the lobby asked all managers to report to the conference room upon arrival. Thaddeus, Ellen, and Marcel grabbed cups of coffee and took seats, side by side.

Mr. Stiller walked into the room, followed by a woman and a man Thaddeus didn't recognize. They took seats in the back as Mr. Stiller walked up to the front.

Mr. Stiller was a good man. He started his company when he was a young twenty-five-year-old. He and his wife had worked very hard together and built a business that now employed more than fifty local people. He was respected. He was loved. But unfortunately, he was also getting older. He and his wife now planned to travel the world and spend their remaining years visiting their grandchildren.

"I'm sure you've all heard the news by this point," Mr. Stiller began.

"I apologize that the story got out to the press, and you didn't hear it from me first. But Marie and I have decided to sell the company."

Murmurs quietly circled the room.

Mr. Stiller raised his hand. The noise faded into silence.

"I want to thank each of you. It's been my honor to work with you over the years. I couldn't have asked for anything more. I know that you're concerned, but Stencil, Osgood, and Broughton have assured me they plan to keep as many employees as possible. Also, Marie and I have decided to give each employee a bonus of five percent of your annual salary. You've helped us build this company. We wanted to do more than just tell you how much we appreciate you. We decided to make it something tangible."

People around the room expressed their thanks.

"At this time, I would like to introduce Ms. Victoria Stencil, president of Stencil, Osgood, and Broughton."

A few people in the room began to applaud, but their efforts quickly faded into an awkward silence.

Ms. Stencil began. "Thank you, Mr. Stiller. You've been a great competitor and we'll miss you. I know your employees will, too."

Turning to the managers, she said, "I know you'll all have many questions…"

His nerves getting the best of him now, and trying to add a little levity to the moment, Thaddeus raised his hand. "I have a question."

Ms. Stencil stopped and looked at Thaddeus. "Alright. Go ahead."

Thaddeus asked, "Would you mind starting this meeting near the end? We're all really anxious to find out how this story turns out."

Everyone laughed. Well, almost everyone.

Ms. Stencil didn't seem to find the question all that humorous.

Zip it, Bud! Or you're going to be on the streets.

Though obviously annoyed, to her credit, Ms. Stencil maintained her demeanor and simply nodded.

"Yes, I will. As concerned as you all must be, that's certainly a reasonable request. We plan to sell this facility. We think we'll be able to offer all of you positions within our company. There'll be some cases where similar positions would result in a duplication we really won't need. So in those cases, we'll try to find you another position. We truly don't want anyone to be unemployed."

After spending a few minutes telling the group about the history of Stencil, Osgood and Broughton, and their business philosophy, Ms. Stencil closed out the meeting by saying, "Have a little faith and give us a chance. We'll do our best. We're going to meet with each of you individually today and start interviews."

She looked at a list of names on a clipboard. "Hmmm. Let's see. We'll start with Thaddeus Tucker." Looking around the room, she asked, "Which one of you is Thad?"

Thaddeus awkwardly raised his hand and said, "That would be me. It's... it's *Thaddeus* Tucker."

Ms. Stencil smiled. "Alright, *Thaddeus*."

Thaddeus held up his hands. "You can thank my mother for that."

Ms. Stencil laughed. Seeing that, the rest of the group relaxed a little and laughed as well.

As everyone filed out of the room, Thaddeus, Ms. Stencil, and the other man took seats at the end of the conference table.

Ms. Stencil began. "Mr. Tucker, you're pretty funny. A sense of humor in the right situation can be a tremendous asset."

Thaddeus replied, "Yes, ma'am." Dropping his head, he added, "And today was not the right situation, I'm guessing. I apologize for that."

Ms. Stencil shook her head. "No, Thaddeus. Today is understandably a stressful day for you. We all handle anxiety in our own way. You can relax about that."

Thaddeus was pleasantly surprised. "Thank you, ma'am."

Ms. Stencil asked, "Would you like to come to work for our company?"

"Honestly, Ms. Stencil. I don't know you guys yet. So, I'm not sure. I guess it will depend on if you have a position for me that pays well and that I'm qualified for."

Ms. Stencil thought for a minute, and said, "Since you're the customer-service manager, what we had in mind for the first ninety days is for you to be our transition coordinator."

"What's a transition coordinator?"

"That's the person who'll visit all of Stiller's clients, explain the buyout, and make sure we don't lose the loyal Stiller customers in the process."

Suddenly, Thaddeus began to have an all-too-familiar feeling. His mouth was again getting ready to overpower his common sense.

"Ms. Stencil?"

"Yes?"

"I have a question."

"Then ask it."

"About twenty-five percent of our customers used to be clients with you all. What do I tell them? How do I get them to give you another chance?"

As soon as the words left his mouth, Thaddeus regretted them. He didn't mean any disrespect. It was a serious attempt for answers. Realizing how it sounded, he tried to add a little laughter in his voice, but the laughter only gave his comments a cynical tone. He knew he'd just made a mistake… a big one.

Ms. Stencil looked down, nodded, then looked back up at Thaddeus. "That certainly could be a challenge, couldn't it, Mr. Tucker?"

Closing her folder, Ms. Stencil said, "Mr. Tucker, we have a customer-service manager already. I'm not sure what other position would be suitable for you. So, just to be safe, I'm going to recommend that you begin a job search now. You'll get paid through the end of the month. But please feel welcome to take the rest of the day off and get started—today."

The man at the other end of the table had stayed silent all morning, and it made Thaddeus uncomfortable. Who was this guy, anyway? Was that a smile on his face?

~ ~ ~

Thinking back on his words from this morning, as he now sat on the park bench, Thaddeus shook his head and stared, dazed, at nothing.

As if on cue, a bird landed on the statue of Louis Armstrong and chirped in Thaddeus's direction as if scolding him.

"I know, I know! I can't believe I said that either!"

This morning, he had a job.

This afternoon, he had free time.

And the sound of his mother's voice echoed through his mind again.

Thaddeus may have had no idea what he was going to do next, but one thing was certain: changes were headed his way like a speeding train.

And he'd just stepped onto the track.

2

The Busker

Livia Aurelia Cole was a breathtaking young woman. Her mother was Creole, her father Jamaican. If there were ever a lottery winner in the genetics category, Livia had received the grand prize. She had an exotic appearance, a brilliant smile, and deep sparkling eyes that would draw people into her kind-hearted nature from the very first glance.

"You're the second most beautiful woman I've ever seen, Livia," said her father on numerous occasions.

"Second? Who'd be the first?" Livia would ask, feigning surprise. She always knew the answer.

Her dad would smile and glance toward her mother.

"That'd be dat woman, right over there. She had more faith in dis man than he ever could. The one dat brought you into dis world, twenty-five years ago…"

"I'm twenty-six, Daddy."

Her father knew her age, but rarely said it correctly. It was funny to him.

It was funny to Livia too.

"What? How'd you get so *oooold?* I know *I* haven't aged twenty-six years since you were born. How could you?"

Livia laughed. "I'm gaining on you, Daddy!"

15

"Dat's right!" Her father laughed, and said, "Remind me how you do the math on dat one."

"Sure, Daddy. When I was one, you were twenty-five. I was exactly four percent of your age. I'm now twenty-six. You're fifty. That makes me fifty-two percent of your age."

Her father nodded. "You *are* aging quickly, aren't you?"

"Yes, sir! At this rate, when I turn sixty-five, I'll pass you."

On this morning, her father had already left for work by the time Livia pulled her cart into the living room. Inside was an amplifier, microphone, and several bottles of water.

From the kitchen, her mother heard Livia, and asked, "Livia! Are you going out to sing today?"

"Yes, ma'am," she replied with a sweet smile.

"Your father will work late today. Mind makin' groceries on your way home?"

Makin' groceries was pure New Orleans. As a matter of fact, if anyone referred to the task as "shopping", or "going to the store", locals shook their heads, grinned, and said, "Tourists!"

"Not at all, Mom," Livia said, as she walked into the kitchen and gave her mother a hug and a kiss on the cheek. "Do you have a list for me?"

"I do," her mother said, tearing the list from a pad attached to the refrigerator. Livia smiled as she saw the image on the magnetic clip—a family heirloom now for over fifteen years. It was a picture of her very first appearance on stage. She had given an absolutely thrilling solo performance of *A Perfect Little Puppy* in the third-grade musical production of *Adopt Me! I'm Too Cute to Pass Up!*

That solo brought the audience to its feet for a standing ovation. Well, at least two people were standing and cheering—her mom and dad. They'd always been her greatest supporters.

She couldn't have asked for better parents.

Livia knew how blessed she was to have such a stable home life. Growing up in what the media often referred to as an *under-resourced community,* she understood not everyone in her neighborhood had that same sense of security.

Her father had often said, "*Under-resourced? We're not under-resourced. Oh no, no, no.* Maybe we don't have a lot of money, but we have enough of the resources that matter the most. Way more than I had as a ragamuffin in Montego Bay. We've got food. We've got work. Most important—we are bless up with love in dis house."

Hugging Livia's mother, he would add, "Me and my *boonoonoonoos* make sure of dat."

Livia loved her father's accent, although it had faded a bit over the years since moving to New Orleans as a teenager. He had a colorful flair for intentionally mixing the local New Orleans dialect with his native Jamaican *patois.*

Boonoonoonoos, a word roughly translated as "sweetheart", was one of her favorites.

Maybe her fondness for the word was because the simple act of saying *"boo—noo—noo—noos,"* was so much fun.

Maybe it was because of the rich and deep tone of her father's voice, which had the timbre of a classically trained bass vocalist reciting the lyrics of a song.

Or maybe it was because of the look on her father's face when he said it. Whether speaking to Livia or her mother, the man's eyes showed total adoration when speaking to his family… his *boonoonoonoos.*

It warmed her soul.

She also loved the music of her father's heritage. The rhythmic style and instrumentation of Jamaican music, especially reggae, always lifted her spirits.

Livia loved their family trips to see her grandparents in Montego Bay. Those journeys cemented lifelong memories of *bashments*—large parties, with people laughing, singing, and dancing.

Oh, yes… and drinking Red Stripe Beer, the national beer of Jamaica.

Her uncle Martin often said, "Ya mon! Do you know why Red Stripe Beer has dis 'DG' ting on the label?" Pointing to the bottle, he said, "Because it *is* DG - Damn Good Beer!" Although she was too young at the time to join in the drinking, she gleefully danced and sang with the group.

In Livia's singing, the rich cultural influences of Jamaica, New Orleans, jazz, R & B and soul came together like the ingredients of a great dish, creating a musical style that remained in the audience's mind long after their melodic dining experience was over.

Her mother handed Livia the grocery list. "Thank you, baby. What time will you be home?"

"I'll catch the lunch crowd, make groceries, and still have plenty of time to get back for the dinner crowd."

Livia's beautiful voice and her singing versatility were unusual. Impossible for most people.

She could effortlessly sing melodies with a soft jazz style. She could improvise a scat solo that would have made Louis Armstrong proud. But she was equally adept at singing reggae, rock, R & B, or hip-hop.

Her parents had never earned a lot of money. But they worked extra shifts, did odd jobs, or sold old household items, so that Livia could take private vocal lessons from a very early age.

"God gave her talent. It's our job to help her grow it," said her mother on Livia's fifth birthday.

Her parents were so proud of her.

Not because of her beauty.

Not because of her talent.

But because of the person she had always been and the adult she had now become.

Her parents told her, "Your looks will fade someday. Your voice may lose its richness. But your kindness, your willingness to expect the best from yourself and see the best in others, and your gentle strength—those are the things that make you who you are, a wonderful young woman that we are so very proud of."

Living at home in her mid-twenties wasn't something Livia planned. She'd thought of getting her own apartment. But her parents encouraged her to not worry about that for now. They wanted her to take this time to focus on making a living as a singer—instead of getting a job to pay for a place to live.

She agreed. But only after they acquiesced to her insistence on paying $1,500 per month in rent. She said, "You two have to let me do that, or I'll need to get a place of my own."

Her parents reluctantly agreed, and Livia had never missed a single payment.

Walking out the door, Livia said, "Bye, Mom."

"Bye, baby. Be careful."

She winked at her mom and said, "Always."

Livia walked down Bourbon Street, taking in the sights and sounds along her route, savoring each step.

New Orleans is filled with many rich and wonderful traditions that give the city its flair. The unique food has its definitive taste, appealing to almost any palate. The architecture spans a myriad of styles, influences, and cultures. And the history of the area inspires both awe and reverence. Walking through the many historical cemeteries and seeing markers of local citizens dating back for hundreds of years gives one a perspective that deeply touches the heart.

But for Livia, New Orleans was all about the music.

It was the birthplace of jazz and the blues. It had been the home of many famous musicians, such as Louis Armstrong and Fats Domino. And Livia loved the French Quarter—its streets filled with clubs where she could hear live music on almost a 24/7 basis.

Many of those famous musicians began their careers as buskers—musicians who performed on the streets. Their income came primarily from tips they would earn from tourists and locals passing by. If on the right corner at the right time, buskers could earn enough to keep a roof over their head, food in their stomach, and even afford a few luxuries now and again—such as a late-night gathering with other street artists at one of the local clubs after they'd all finished their performances for the evening.

Livia was a busker—and a good one at that.

Her rich voice and gentle nature effortlessly drew crowds around her. She captivated them with her elegant renditions of jazz classics. She surprised them with her repertoire of reggae and hip-hop. And she often finished with her original compositions.

On this morning, as had been the case for almost a month now, Livia rolled her cart to the corner of Royal Street and St. Louis Street, in front of the Judge Fred J. Cassibry Square. She set up her amplifier, microphone, and her tip bag, placing each on the ground in front of her. One by one, she placed items into their exact positions, in a display she often convinced herself was for the crowd to enjoy.

Truth be told, it was only a little about the crowd.

Mostly, it reflected Livia's desire to have an order to the things around her.

A place for everything and everything in its place.

She sat on the retaining wall, chose music from her smartphone, and then gave the surrounding crowd a musical experience that was delightful and well appreciated. After each song, she gave a shy smile to the crowd as they applauded and dropped money into the bag on the ground.

Livia was at peace.

She had parents who were supportive and gave her unconditional love. She lived in a city that filled her yearning for music and culture. And she was earning a living—a modest living—singing.

For most of the buskers in New Orleans, crowds are primarily comprised of people who stop for just a few minutes, applaud when appropriate, then drop a dollar or two into the busker's tip bucket. The crowds rarely stay around for a full song unless the busker also has someone working the crowd to keep them in the vicinity longer.

20

However, the musical experience with Livia was different.

She needed no one to keep the crowd engaged with her performance. Her voice did that well. People planned to pass on by. But once hearing the exceptional melodies coming from this beautiful woman, they found themselves staying longer to enjoy the music. Many stayed so long that by the time Livia finished her forty-five-minute set, the sidewalk was completely full of people, and it was difficult for anyone else to proceed.

Livia had also shown a bit of business savvy in her young busker career. She had a sign professionally printed with links and QR codes that would allow her benefactors to use their smartphones to tip for her performance. Effortless and convenient.

"Touchless Tipping" was printed across the top of the sign with bold colors. Below the title, Livia's sign said, "If Livia has added to your enjoyment of New Orleans, you are welcome to take selfies and videos with her as she sings and share them on your social-media platforms. Please use the hashtag, #lovingliviainNOLA, and we will say hello to your friends too. For your convenience, if you're so inclined, please tip with cash or your favorite cash app. Both your financial kindness and your sharing Livia with the world is greatly appreciated."

The sign worked well... very well. Livia was surprised. Her income had more than doubled almost instantaneously. Although many still tipped in cash, the crowds seemed to love the convenience of the payment choices and the sanitary nature of a touchless system. Livia loved that she didn't have to carry so much cash around. She'd never been robbed. But she was always a little wary of her surroundings as she gathered her tips.

As she finished her first song, there were already eight people gathered around—phones raised high—filming.

Of course, New Orleans boasts a tremendous tourism industry. As a result, Livia would sometimes see posts from people around the world. They were sharing their good times, the sights and sounds of the city, and Livia's performances. She didn't check social-media often. But when she did, it made her smile.

21

A couple in the crowd asked, "Is your music available for purchase online?"

"No. I've never really done that. Producing the music would be very expensive. And for me, the fun part is sitting out here with y'all and enjoying each other's company."

Even though Livia was telling the truth, or at least part of the truth, there was much more to the story than her answer revealed.

The music business was tough. Record companies didn't just give young buskers a contract with loads of cash and limousines. For the most part, they simply turned buskers down, and not always in a polite manner. The thought of someone rejecting Livia's singing was very unsettling to her. Her music came straight from her heart. It felt as if they were rejecting her *personally*... instead of making a simple business decision that didn't go her way.

In her heart, she knew she had talent. She wasn't afraid of hard work. And she knew that the people surrounding her loved the experience. But even if a record label agreed to produce, distribute, and promote her music—they would also keep the lion's share of her royalties. That all gave her doubts about even asking. It was a cutthroat business. And Livia wanted neither her throat, nor her business, cut.

She was excellent at what she did. The crowds loved her. But she also had a bit of self-doubt to contend with.

How can I expect someone else to believe in me when I struggle with that myself?

Livia loved her music. She loved her city. And she loved performing to her audience on the corner in front of the park.

She really wasn't looking for anything more from life at the moment.

But life can be surprising. Events were already in motion that would indeed bring Livia more than she'd ever dreamed.

3

You Believed in Me

Victoria Stencil stretched her shoulders and back, sat straight up, and sighed as she closed her notepad. It was only four o'clock, but the day had been long and draining.

"We've seen all the managers now. What do you think?" she asked the man who had remained silent throughout the morning.

Andre Broughton looked down and considered the question.

Andre began his career with, what was previously called, Stencil and Osgood Benefits, some twenty years earlier. He had been an overconfident, athletic, and at times charming young man straight out of college. He was tall, muscular, and had broad shoulders.

Andre was competitive. During his younger years, he'd been an amateur boxer—a standout in his sport. His height and reach gave him the ability to connect a punch with most opponents without allowing them to get close to him.

He was fearless.

He wanted to win.

As a teen, he'd been an angry young man on the streets of New Orleans. He expected trouble and often found it. Fortunately, he'd been influenced by some great coaches and mentors along the way who'd helped him leave that part of his life behind. However, when he started his sales career with Stencil and Osgood, he still had a few anger issues to deal with.

Now, he'd worked his way up through the ranks, and was the vice president of sales. He had equity ownership in the company, and became a named partner in Stencil, Osgood, and *Broughton*.

Having the name Broughton added to the company stationary also came with the stewardship of the company's New Orleans location.

"I think we can use each of them in jobs close to what they have now," replied Andre.

Victoria said, "I think so too. I'm glad. I don't want this acquisition to hurt the employees. They're why Stiller was so successful. He made such great connections with them. They were family to him and his wife. The bond he forged was almost unbreakable. I want us to strive to do the same."

Andre said, "I visited with Mr. Stiller about that. I asked him why he thought his team was so loyal."

"What'd he say?"

"There were two particular things that I keyed in on. I found them to be very insightful."

Andre stopped to think.

"Don't leave me hanging here, Andre," Victoria said with a smile.

Andre said, "The first thing he said was that today's greatest leaders understand that, as the leader, they're simply the head server, creating the environment for those they lead to thrive. When it came to his company structure, he never viewed himself as sitting *at the top of a pyramid*. He wasn't riding through life on the shoulders of his employees. Instead, he saw his position as being at the bottom of an *upside-down* pyramid—his team on his shoulders. He considered it his responsibility to create an atmosphere where they could build the life they wanted for their families by working at Stiller. He wanted to be a part of their success."

Victoria nodded. "He taught his managers to think the same way."

Andre said, "The second thing he said that really stuck with me was that he'd studied the science of how people make decisions. He then applied that science to create business and leadership processes that influence how some very important decisions are made."

"Such as?"

"Such as how prospects make the decision to listen to the initial offer instead of just saying, 'No thanks.' How those prospects then make the decision to become customers and eventual walking ambassadors for his brand. And most important in Stiller's eyes—how his team members made the decision that Stiller was the place they wanted to stay. It was their home."

Victoria asked, "What do you mean?"

Andre shook his head. "I'm no expert on the subject, by any means. But Mr. Stiller has kindly agreed to help me learn more. I just need to hurry and do so before he and his wife leave for their around-the-world yearlong holiday."

Victoria said, "Keep me posted on that, please."

Andre nodded.

"Victoria?"

"Yes."

"I want to keep that young man from this morning and put him on my sales team."

"What?" replied Victoria, truly surprised.

Andre looked at the list of names in front of him.

"Tucker. Thaddeus Tucker. The first guy we talked with."

"You want *him*?"

"Yes."

"Why?"

"I'm not sure I can pinpoint the reason." He thought for a second. "Maybe I liked the way he said what he was thinking."

"*Without* thinking is more like it."

Andre laughed. "Yeah, but I have a sense that he isn't afraid of many things, has a good head on his shoulders, and as I look at his work history, I think he'll be trainable."

"That's a big ask, Andre. I don't see the same potential in him you do." Shaking her head, Victoria said, "He'd have to learn so much."

Andre just looked at Victoria and smiled. She raised an eyebrow.

"Twenty years ago, many people didn't think I had what it took to make it in sales, either. But one woman took an interest in me and gave me a chance. She then mentored and coached me over the years. I applied what she taught me and became successful. But, had she never given me a chance... had she never taken me on as a protégé, I wouldn't be here today."

She couldn't debate that point any further.

Victoria was that person. She had given Andre his start and mentored him along the way. The two had become great friends and partners over the years.

"Okay, I'll trust your judgment. After all, you're the one who'll be dealing with him. It's your call."

"Done," said Andre. "I'll call him."

Victoria said, "Wait until the end of the day, if you don't mind, Andre. I'd like for him to have a little more time to consider this morning's meeting. I think it may help him be more open to your offer."

Andre chuckled, nodded, and said, "Will do."

4

Rosario Boudreaux's

Thaddeus looked at his watch.

Four o'clock? I had no idea how late it was.

He'd just spent the last two hours looking over various online job postings in the area. He'd saved a few, deleted some, and even made a few phone calls to see if he could schedule interviews. Each phone call proceeded in much the same way.

"I'm sorry, Mr. Tucker. But we don't schedule interviews with anyone before they complete the online application and submit their resume."

"Okay. Thanks."

Well, tomorrow I'll refresh my resume and complete some applications. But not today. I think I'll walk over to the Quarter and grab an early dinner.

One of Thaddeus's favorite restaurants in New Orleans was a little dive on the corner of St. Louis and Royal Street called Rosario Boudreaux's. It was an unusual place that fused some of the greatest recipes of Italian and Cajun cuisines. The menu presented traditional dishes as well as vegan and vegetarian choices. Most interesting to Thaddeus, the eatery combined the time-honored tastes of multiple cultures. Thaddeus's choice was almost always their vegan eggplant parmesan. The chef prepared the meal in the traditional way, for the most part. However, the added Cajun spices definitely gave the dish a unique flavor which was found nowhere else. And somehow, the chef created a vegan version of the dish.

I can walk over to Rosario's and be there by four thirty. I'll beat the dinner crowd.

Thaddeus certainly loved the food at Rosario Boudreaux's, but his favorite thing about the place was their balcony. Large umbrellas shaded the tables. Fans and coolers kept diners comfortable even when dining *alfresco* in August. And the view reminded him of the best box seats in a concert hall.

Thaddeus took great pride in the food of New Orleans. The stylistic blends—especially in the Quarter—were simply delicious. They easily matched any dish from the greatest culinary minds. But for him, music was the crowning jewel of the city.

From Rosario's balcony, he enjoyed the sights and sounds of street musicians and tourists on the street below. There were Dixieland bands, bucket bangers, singers, and ensembles of varying eclectic instrumentation.

Thaddeus originally pursued music as his career. He'd even played professionally in a Dixieland band as he worked his way through his first three years of college. The path he'd planned to follow had been to teach in the New Orleans area, supplementing that income with a side-hustle of busking.

His music education stopped abruptly during his junior year of college, when his father passed away. After the funeral, Thaddeus returned to the university only long enough to tell his friends goodbye, pack his things, and withdraw from his courses.

His mother had told him, "You don't need to move back home, Thaddeus. I'll be fine." However, he believed he needed to be there, both for her emotional and financial support.

His mother was correct. She would've been fine… or at least as fine as anyone who'd just lost a spouse could be. But he was so glad that he came back to spend that time with her. Her last ten years—

years they'd spent together—were at the heart of some of Thaddeus's favorite memories.

As he sat on the balcony, lost in thoughts of his mother, the server sat a plate in front of him.

"Vegan eggplant parmesan with a side of stewed okra and tomatoes. Want a refill on your wine, Thaddeus?"

"I don't think so. Thanks, Martine."

Martine and Thaddeus had known each other since middle school. She was a good friend with a wicked sense of humor. When dining at Rosario's, if Martine was there, he would always request a seat in her section. He enjoyed combining a splendid meal and a visit with a long-time and cherished friend.

"Why are you here so early today? Aren't you normally at work until around six?" asked Martine.

"Yes, I am. But today… well, let's just say that…"

"You got your ass fired, didn't you?" she asked with a look that let him know she was not surprised.

Thaddeus just looked at her with a hint of an embarrassed smile.

"Come on. Out with it. What did you say *this* time? What did you do?" she asked, laughing.

After he recounted the day's events, he asked in his usual light-hearted, yet sarcastic way, "So… you think… maybe I should've handled that differently?"

"Oh no, no, no!" replied Martine, still laughing. "If your goal was to get yourself into the unemployment line, then you handled that perfectly!"

"Well, that wasn't my actual *goal*. It was more like my mouth ran on a few yards ahead of my brain and said too much before I could catch up with it and slam it shut."

"Mm hmm," replied Martine. "Wish I could've seen that! It's not every day that you see a man put his foot into his mouth so far that his toes tickle his tonsils!"

Thaddeus replied, "It wasn't pretty."

With a serious look, Martine said, "I'm sure it wasn't. I'm guessing it was like seeing an awful crash on a street corner. You know, Thaddeus, they say that your perception of time slows down in an accident. Did that scene run in slow motion for you?"

Dropping her voice and speaking in long, drawn-out syllables, as if reducing the playback speed of an audio recording. "Did you ask, 'Coooooould youuuuu start this meeeeeting near the eeeeeend?'"

She laughed. Thaddeus didn't.

"Very funny," he said, managing a slight smile.

"What were you thinking? I can just imagine what your mama would have said."

"Me too. I've been hearing her voice in my mind all afternoon."

Martine laughed and said, "I can hear it now!" Putting both hands on her hips, she said, "'Son, do you *ever* engage your brain before you put your mouth in gear?'"

Thaddeus's smile grew.

"Or, 'Thaddeus Tucker! I raised you better than that. You must have gotten that mouth from your father, God rest his soul!'"

Thaddeus laughed and lifted his eyebrows. "That one would be true, actually."

"And my personal favorite, 'Young man, God gave you common sense. Did you send it back for a refund?'"

"Jolie definitely had her moments. I'm sure she would say that today was not one of my better performances."

Martine turned to move on to her other tables, but stopped and looked back at Thaddeus.

"You came to the right place today. Not only do you get to see me," she said with a certain amount of pride, "you're also going to hear some really great music."

Martine nodded toward the street corner, where a young busker was setting up for the evening.

"She's been coming here for a couple of weeks now. She's my absolute favorite around here. You're gonna love her."

30

Thaddeus smiled as he turned to look. "That'll be a welcome relief from my day."

As he ate his meal, the young lady started singing. Martine was right. Her voice was enchanting, and her choices of music meshed perfectly with his personal tastes.

Martine returned. "Are you ready for your check?"

"I think I'll stay a little longer. Wanna bring me another glass of that chianti?"

"Sure thing."

As she turned to walk away, Thaddeus asked, "Hey, Martine. Who is she? She's incredible!"

Turning back, she said, "I don't know her name. But guess what?"

"What?" he replied.

"Good news! Your brain is apparently returning from its morning vacation. That's the smartest thing you've said all day."

They both laughed as Martine walked away.

Thaddeus sat back, relaxed, and listened for the next hour. He was enjoying the serenity of the moment. However, the buzz of his cell phone interrupted.

Looking at the screen, he saw a number he didn't recognize. Normally, he wouldn't have answered such a call. He assumed they were sales calls, scam calls, or wrong numbers, and would just let the call go to voicemail.

However, today, the music and the wine had mellowed his attitude just enough that he took the call.

"Hello. This is Thaddeus."

"Hi, Thaddeus. Andre Broughton here."

Thaddeus recognized neither the voice nor the name.

"Okay. What can I do for you, Andre? Do we know each other?"

"Not exactly. I came in with Victoria Stencil this morning for your meeting at Stiller."

"Well, that explains why I didn't recognize your voice. You never said anything."

"That's true," replied Andre, with a chuckle.

"So, what can I do for you, Mr. Broughton?"

"This morning, Ms. Stencil told you we may not have a position for you. And, if customer service is where you want to stay, she's right."

Thaddeus continued to listen.

"But if you're open to other opportunities, I'd like to visit with you. I'm the vice president of sales. I run the New Orleans branch, and I may have something for you with me."

Thaddeus thought for a second.

Andre asked, "Are you there, Thaddeus?"

"Sorry. Yes, I'm here. Mr. Broughton…"

"Please, call me Andre."

"Okay, Andre. I'm here. But I don't have any background in sales, nor have I ever really had an interest in going in that direction. Are you sure you wanna talk to *me*?"

"Yes, I'm sure." replied Andre. "Thaddeus, I didn't have any sales experience either when I began my career at Stencil and Osgood. But someone took an interest in me and gave me a chance. With the right training and work ethic, I built a great future for myself and my family."

Andre added, "I really can't promise you anything, and there's certainly no obligation on your part, because I'm not certain that this will be the right position for you. But I'm one-hundred percent certain that you and I will be the two best people to make that determination. I'd like to invite you to drop by my office for a visit tomorrow so that we can explore the possibility."

Thaddeus replied, "Okay. Thank you. What time?"

"Be here at nine o'clock, unless you already have something going on. I'll text you the address."

Thaddeus laughed and said, "No. As of this morning, an unexpected gap opened up in my calendar for tomorrow."

Andre laughed as well. "Sounds good. See you then."

He disconnected the call.

Thaddeus paid his check and went downstairs and out onto the street. He walked over to the young street singer and dropped a tip into her bag.

"Your music is as lovely as you are. Thank you so much for making my afternoon much more enjoyable than I expected."

Livia gave Thaddeus a smile… but with a bit of trepidation in her eyes.

Realizing how his compliment may have sounded flirtatious, he raised his palms, and said, "I used to play on these same streets, and I have a genuine appreciation for great music."

He saw her eyes relax a little.

"Thank you," she said.

He said nothing else. He just nodded and walked away. Still, he heard her music in his mind. Rhythmic. Flowing. Smooth.

He knew himself. As soon as his head rested on his pillow that night, his thoughts would race through the fiasco of the morning. And even with the dramatic turn of events this afternoon—the lifeline Andre had thrown him—he doubted sleep would come.

But for now, Thaddeus simply savored the moment.

┌─────────┐
│ **5** │
└─────────┘

The Second Chance

T haddeus walked into the offices of Stencil, Osgood, and Broughton at 8:45 a.m..

Fifteen minutes early, he thought. *I messed up enough yesterday! Doing everything right today.*

He approached the reception desk where a young man was sitting. Thaddeus waited patiently as the man finished a phone call.

"My apologies, sir. Welcome to Stencil, Osgood, and Broughton. My name is Henry. How may I best assist you today?"

"Thank you," replied Thaddeus. "I have a nine o'clock appointment with Andre Broughton. I'm a little early. I don't mind waiting."

"I'll check to see if Mr. Broughton is ready for you." Gesturing over to a beautiful area in the lobby's corner, equipped with various coffee blends and drinks in a refrigerator, Henry said, "Please feel welcome to get a bottle of water or other refreshment at the counter while I check."

"Thank you," said Thaddeus.

"My pleasure!"

Thaddeus was remarkably calm. This surprised him.

Shouldn't I be nervous? This is a job interview... and I need a job.

He didn't know if his calm spirit resulted from his mindset—that he wasn't qualified for a sales job, nor was he sure he even wanted one—or maybe it was because the meeting itself was a definite step up from yesterday's fiasco.

But after more introspection, Thaddeus decided his calmness came as a direct result of the words Andre used.

"*I really can't promise you anything, and there's certainly no obligation on your part...*" That's how Andre had phrased it.

That's why I'm so calm. He took the pressure off by how he asked. He took me off the hook. And instead of asking me to come in for a meeting, he invited me to drop by for a visit.

Before his thoughts could carry him further, Henry's voice interrupted.

"Mr. Tucker, Mr. Broughton will see you now."

"Thank you, Henry. And please, call me Thaddeus."

"Certainly, Thaddeus. Right this way."

Thaddeus followed Henry past several offices, a conference room, and a break room. Finally, after proceeding through a long hallway, Henry gestured to an open door that led to Andre's office.

"Thank you for leading the way, Henry! I'm not sure that I would've found it."

"My pleasure, Thaddeus!" said Henry as he closed the door and left the room.

Thaddeus scanned the office. The walls were bare, except for one framed print that said:

~

You can't make a six-figure income
on minimum-wage effort

~

There was a small conference table, a brown leather sofa, and boxes scattered around, needing to be unpacked.

Behind the desk along the far wall, Andre was already getting up and walking over to his guest.

"Good morning, Thaddeus! How are you?"

"Good morning, sir! Doing quite well, thank you. And you?"

"Doing great, thanks!"

Looking around the office and noting the boxes, Andre said, "Please excuse the mess. I was given the responsibility for this branch only last month. I haven't quite gotten settled in yet."

"Where'd you move in from?"

Andre replied, "About four doors past the break room." Then he smiled and added, "I'm from New Orleans."

Thaddeus laughed.

"Wow! Taking over a branch office *and* facilitating the buyout of a new company at the same time? Andre, in thinking about the next months, I only have one suggestion for you."

"What's that?"

"You'll need to find something to do with all of your spare time!"

Both men laughed.

Andre gestured toward the conference table.

"Please, have a seat."

The men sat down, and the interview began.

"So tell me your story, Thaddeus. Tell me what's brought you to this point."

Thaddeus smirked. "Well, if you're talking about what brought me to the point of looking for a job… yesterday, I allowed my mouth to do too much while my brain did too little. As a result, I got fired. You may have heard about it. It was an epic disaster! I'm sure it had to be on the local news."

Andre nodded. "It *was* on the news. I think they said something like, *Local Man Breaks Record for Shortest Career with New Company.*"

"Not my finest hour."

"I'm sure. As a matter of fact, let's just get that issue behind us. Should we both determine that this is a great opportunity for you, and you'd fit into our company culture, the first thing I need to teach you is that at birth, you were given exactly one brain, two ears, and one mouth. You need to inform your mouth that your brain is in charge, your ears are second in command, and your chops have only a minority voting share."

Thaddeus laughed. He wondered if Andre also had a musical background. Using the word *chops,* instead of the word *mouth,* was something he knew musicians did.

Andre gave Thaddeus a look that conveyed both caring and an expectation of better results in the future. He said, "Your brain is your boss. Your ears and eyes are gathering intel to bring back to the boss."

He paused, then added, "And your mouth needs to learn that unless it's helping the ears gather intel, or helping the boss put forth helpful suggestions, it should probably remain the silent partner. Catch my drift?"

Thaddeus's eyes dropped. "Yes, sir. I do." Then he looked at Andre and said, "Mama tried, but apparently it didn't take. I apologize. Thank you for being willing to take a second look at me."

"Apology accepted. My pleasure. Now, you can put that behind you and learn from it rather than worry about it."

There was a kindness, paired with a firmness, that gave Thaddeus good feelings about Andre. Feelings he hadn't expected.

Thaddeus took a few minutes to tell Andre about his experience, education, and family details. The questions Andre asked, combined with the way he asked them and how he was actively listening to the answers, made it clear he wasn't just interviewing Thaddeus for a job. He wanted to know more about him as a person.

"Thaddeus, I'll get into what a job in sales will look like in a bit. But first, there's a question I'd like to hear you answer. And I want you to take a few minutes to think about it before you do."

Curious, Thaddeus replied, "Alright. Thinking, before I answer? Hmm, I like that concept."

Andre laughed, and asked, "If I could wave a magic wand and create the perfect career for you, what would it look like? Don't answer

38

with a job title. Instead, give me a job description, or maybe even a life description. Paint a word picture for me.

"I'll give you a minute to gather your thoughts while I refresh my coffee. May I get you some?"

"Thank you, no."

Andre left the room, and Thaddeus began to think.

That may be the most unusual job-interview question I've ever been asked.

When Andre returned, he sat back down and asked, "So, what do you think? Can you describe that ideal career for me?"

"Maybe," said Thaddeus, looking down at a notepad he'd brought.

"I wrote down five words. *Lifestyle. Competence. Meaningful. Local.* And *Environment.* They aren't in any particular order, and the list probably isn't complete, but those are a pretty good start."

Looking over the list, Andre asked, "So, what do those words mean to you?"

"*Lifestyle…* of course, the career would need to provide well so that I can build the life I want. I would eventually like to get married and have children. I don't want to worry about money."

"Okay," said Andre, as he nodded.

"*Competence…* I don't know that I can be specific about the activities themselves. But the day-to-day details have to be something I can learn, and feel competent doing them. Seeing myself as inept sets off uncomfortable feelings in me. Those feelings can cause me to fail to take action, get nervous, or…"

"Or talk too much?" asked Andre with a smile.

Thaddeus was a little embarrassed, but liked Andre's humor. He crinkled his nose. "Point taken."

Andre replied, "I apologize. My bad. I just couldn't help myself. I had to bite my lip yesterday to keep from laughing."

Thaddeus remembered seeing that.

"Because it was funny?"

"No. Because I couldn't believe anyone would say those things. I couldn't decide if you were brave or naïve."

Both laughed.

"Keep going," said Andre.

"*Meaningful*... I'd like to feel that my work really mattered and wasn't just a way to make a living."

Andre nodded.

"*Local*... I love New Orleans and I want to stay here."

"And *environment*... I want the place I work, and the people I work with, to be an environment that gives me a sense of pride and happiness just because I work there. Maybe a sense of belonging?"

Andre thought for a moment.

"Thaddeus, I've got some good news for you. The things you just described, which would be involved in your ideal career, match reasonably well with the things that this position offers you."

"Really?"

"Yes. You mentioned that the career would need to pay enough for you to build the life you want. In this company, salespeople who do their jobs well are among the top earners in the US. Additionally, I teach a financial management class for our employees that will help you manage your money—a very important skill for a salesperson on commission."

Thaddeus raised his eyebrows. He wasn't particularly adept at handling his finances.

"You said that you needed to feel competent. That part's on both of us. You'll have to do the work. But I'll personally educate you and be your field trainer. I just took over this branch. I'd really love to have someone who'll do exactly what I teach them. When they do, they'll become highly successful and give me an example to spotlight for the entire team."

"Okay," said Thaddeus.

Andre paused, then said, "As for meaningful... we connect our clients with companies that provide money to prevent medical difficul-

40

ties from becoming financial hardships for their families. When you meet some of our policyholders and see the gratitude in their eyes as you help them… I think you'll find the whole process makes you feel good about what you'll be doing."

Andre added, "As for local… the job is here in New Orleans, of course. And as for the work environment, I'm really glad to hear you say that."

"Why?"

"That's the biggest area that this branch needs to improve upon. I want to build that exact culture you described. Y'all had that in droves at Stiller. I want to create that here, as well. As a matter of fact, I'm meeting with Mr. Stiller for lunch today. I'd like for him to mentor me on how he accomplished that." He added, "I really like that man!"

"Me too," replied Thaddeus.

Thaddeus thought, *Okay. I'm impressed with this guy. He's obviously good at what he's doing. But he's humble enough to seek help too.*

"Alright, Andre. Can you show me what salespeople do and how you're gonna get me up to speed?"

"No."

Surprised, Thaddeus asked, "No?"

Andre smiled. "No. But I *can* show you how you and I'll work together to get you up to speed. How's that?"

The rest of the interview was spent with Andre walking Thaddeus through the day-to-day activities, the mindset of a salesperson, and the training program.

"Do you have any questions?" Andre asked.

Thaddeus replied, "Not yet. I'm sure I will as I digest the information we've discussed."

Andre stood and extended his hand. Thaddeus did the same.

"Thaddeus, do you see any reason you wouldn't want to move forward with this?"

"No, surprisingly enough, I don't. When do I start?"

Andre shook his head. "Hold on. I'd like for you to think about this for a bit, then get back to me. I'd like to have you on my team. I think you'll do well. If, after a day or two, you still think it's something you'd like to do, then we'll welcome you aboard. Fair enough?"

Thaddeus replied, "Yes, sir. It is, indeed. Thank you for meeting with me this morning."

"My pleasure, Thaddeus. Thank you for coming in."

Andre grabbed his keys from the corner of the desk.

"I'll walk out with you. I'm leaving now as well... going to visit with Mr. Stiller."

Thaddeus said, "Please tell him I said hello."

"I certainly will. I'm looking forward to spending time with him. He was doing so many things right. The loyalty he generated with his clients and employees has been amazing. I can't wait to learn some of his secrets."

Thaddeus agreed. "That's Mr. Stiller, alright. He's been a great example to me and so many others. I'm not at all surprised that he's willing to help you."

As Andre started to get into his car and head out for his meeting with Mr. Stiller, Thaddeus said, "Hey Andre?"

"Yes?"

"Thanks again. I'll be calling you on Monday."

"I look forward to it." replied Andre as he got into his car and drove away.

6

Fusion Points™

Walking into the door of the restaurant, Andre immediately saw Mr. Stiller sitting at a table, drinking coffee and enjoying the panoramic view of the Mississippi River.

Standing, Mr. Stiller said, "Good morning, Andre!"

"Good morning, Mr. Stiller! Thanks so much for meeting with me!"

"My pleasure! Please, have a seat."

The two men exchanged pleasantries and ordered their lunch.

After a few minutes of small talk, Andre said, "Mr. Stiller, from what I've seen, the level of loyalty you've generated in the marketplace and with your employees has been the best I've found anywhere."

"Thank you, Andre. That's very kind of you to say."

Andre replied, "My pleasure. But it's not just kindness. It is an observation I've made and I'm quite impressed."

Mr. Stiller smiled, but seemed almost embarrassed.

"Mr. Stiller, I have a confession to make."

With a kind look, Mr. Stiller asked, "What?"

Andre replied, "I'm really good at my job. I can sell. I can coach and teach others to do the same. I can put systems in place and create logical training programs to transfer the skills to my team…" Andre paused.

"But?" asked Mr. Stiller.

"But… I don't think I've ever built the kind of loyalty I've seen with you. It's one of the reasons your company has done so well."

Mr. Stiller nodded.

Andre added, "That's a skill that I need to develop. I'm confident enough to know that I can. But I also know that there's a lot I need to learn in order to become the leader I want to be. I need a mentor to show me the way. So, thank you for doing this."

"I'm glad to help. My pleasure."

Andre said, "When we visited last week, you mentioned two things to me. The first was how you viewed your organization as an upside-down pyramid."

Mr. Stiller said, "That's correct. Although there could certainly be more, I generally see two distinctive styles of leadership in most organizations. The first group seems to act as if they view their customers and their team as being part of a pyramid—and see themselves positioned on the top. They are more directive than collaborative. They see their team as working *for* them rather than *with* them. And they view customers as something they must acquire and accumulate in order to have a successful business, instead of being their partners."

Andre pulled out a pad and pen. He asked, "Mr. Stiller, would you mind if I take some notes?"

"Not at all." replied Mr. Stiller.

"Please continue." said Andre.

Mr. Stiller said, "The challenge with that type of leadership view, in my opinion, is that it's focused in the wrong direction. Also, being perched atop a pyramid is precarious. One can easily tumble off… or even worse, get impaled!"

The two men winced at the thought.

Mr. Stiller thought for a second, then added. "The second type of leader would be those who view their organizational structure as being

44

an *upside-down* pyramid. They view their team and their customers as being on *their* shoulders. They look for ways to support, equip, and provide value to them. That's the leadership style I believe to be the best."

Andre asked, "Does that ever result in execution issues? Aren't there times when you just need to tell people what they should do and have them go do it, especially when they aren't succeeding?"

Mr. Stiller replied, "There'll still be times where you'll need to have difficult conversations with some people. However, if the issue isn't their work ethic or their attitude, you can approach the discussion differently."

Andre asked, "Approach it how?"

Mr. Stiller replied, "Instead of telling them *what* to do, you can often give them a target. Show them the results that are needed, and then get them involved in the *what to do* part. If they're involved in planning how to achieve the results, they'll take ownership. More importantly, they'll take pride in that ownership, which strengthens their skill set and their bond with you."

"I see," said Andre, thinking back on some difficult conversations that he'd handled poorly. With his athletic background, he often found himself communicating like one of his favorite coaches, direct, blunt and at times, too strong. Fortunately, Victoria had seen what was happening.

One day, she walked into his office, laid a whistle on his desk, and said, "Be careful, Andre. You're an athlete. You're used to being motivated by people who could be confrontational and intimidating. That's fine for you. But others on your team may not relate to that style. Focus on what they need from you to become better at their jobs. And work with them in a way that draws them toward you, rather than pushes them away."

Andre said, "Mr. Stiller, I've struggled with that in the past. I'm getting better now, but still a work in progress."

Mr. Stiller nodded. then said, "The same goes with customers. Some leaders look at their customer base as a group of assets that they *own*. I see things differently. I see customers as our partners. They have needs that, when solved, create a better situation for them personally or professionally. Our job is to take responsibility for helping them do exactly that. That's part of the value that we bring to the table. We serve them. And the more people we serve, the more we're able to succeed and take care of our families the way we desire."

Andre said, "When I think about that, it makes so much sense to me. I can see why people see you as a leader they'd want to follow. Our human nature draws us toward people who we believe have our best interest at heart."

Mr. Stiller replied, "It's great for them to *believe* it. But we want them to *know* it. Our job as leaders is to take that belief, and make it grow."

Andre nodded. "Something else you mentioned that I find fascinating is that you've studied the *science* of how people make decisions. Then you applied that science to develop your processes."

"Right," replied Mr. Stiller.

Andre smiled, lifted his hands, and gave a quizzical look.

"How?"

Mr. Stiller replied, "Several years ago I attended a workshop on the subject—*Fusion Points™: Engage the Science of Persistence*. In the few minutes we have here today, I'll only be able to give you the highlights."

"I'll take what I can get at this point," replied Andre.

Mr. Stiller explained, "There is a science—an actual neurological process—that occurs in the brain with each and every decision we humans make. There are no exceptions."

Andre wrote the word, science, and drew a brain on his pad.

"When we apply that science in our sales and customer-service models, our team-retention plans, and even in our personal pursuits, we can influence how some very important decisions are made."

"Important decisions?" asked Andre. "Such as?"

"We can influence how a prospect makes the decision to listen to our offer rather than saying 'Thanks, but no thanks.' We can influence how a potential buyer decides to become our customer and eventual walking ambassador. And we can influence how we, as salespeople and entrepreneurs, decide to be tenacious and persist in our chosen profession."

Andre grinned and said, "That would be a valuable skill to develop."

Mr. Stiller said, "It would indeed. But even more importantly, as company leaders, we can influence how our team members decide to stay with us, instead of defecting to our competitors, or leaving sales completely."

"What type of influence are you talking about?" Andre asked.

"Great question, Andre. I'm not talking about anything resembling manipulation, where one is attempting to influence another selfishly. Instead, I'm talking about influencing their decisions by creating mutually beneficial win-win scenarios, in which the other person feels completely at ease with taking the next step in our process. People are drawn toward you instead of pushing away from you."

Andre lifted his hands and asked, "So, what is the science behind this?"

Mr. Stiller replied, "Every decision we make is actually a combination of logic and emotion. One area of the brain processes the logic. A different part of the brain processes the emotion. Those two regions communicate, weigh the options, and produce a result—a decision that we then act upon. Although we'd all like to think we make purely logical decisions, neurologists will tell you it doesn't work that way."

Andre laughed. "Looking back on some of the decisions I made in my youth... I'm not sure logic played any role at all."

Mr. Stiller smiled. "That's because the emotional part of the brain also throws a couple of curveballs at us."

"How's that?" asked Andre.

47

"Every emotion we experience produces a somatic marker—a physiological response. We literally experience a distinct feeling inside our body because of something happening in our brain. Certain emotions—I'll call them negative emotions—like anger, fear, frustration, loneliness, and anxiety, produce somatic markers we dislike. We link that uncomfortable feeling inside us with the activities that are happening at that moment. We want to avoid them from that point forward, by either running away from the activity, or becoming confrontational."

Andre said, "I think I know exactly what you're talking about. I was quite angry with the world as a teen. The feelings those emotions created inside me often caused me to lash out."

"That's very observant, Andre."

Mr. Stiller continued, "Other emotions—*positive* emotions—such as love, joy, a sense of belonging, and contentment also produce somatic markers that we link to whatever activity is happening at the time. But in this case, we like that feeling inside us and want to keep the activity going."

Andre asked, "So, how do we use that science to influence decisions?"

Mr. Stiller replied, "Most companies have many logical processes that are used in their business. Their sales process has a step-by-step system that, when followed, should produce new clients. Their customer-service model is methodical and should work well to keep those clients. And their training on the day-to-day business functions should equip their employees to succeed."

He paused, then added, "That should all work perfectly well, right? After all, it's logical."

Andre nodded. He took pride in how he structured the training of new sales people. It was, as Mr. Spock might say—raising an eyebrow, "Logical."

Mr. Stiller said, "The trouble is, it just doesn't work that way. Companies can spend millions of dollars on training programs, customer-retention plans, and employee-retention efforts, and still have high turnover and low results."

"Why?" asked Andre.

"Because they only address the logic of how any decision is made. They ignore the emotional component."

"So, how should I address both the logical and emotional sides of the equation?" asked Andre.

Mr. Stiller replied, "When logic and negative emotions combine, they create a collision point. Collision points cause prospects, customers, and employees to be hesitant in moving forward with you and your company. However, when logic and positive emotions combine, fusion points occur. When that happens, prospects are more likely to say yes. Customers become loyal ambassadors for your brand. And employees don't want to work for anyone else."

Mr. Stiller leaned in and said, "Your job, Andre, is to be intentional. Analyze your processes. Neutralize any collision points that you can. Then create, add, and optimize fusion points throughout your business model."

"Can you give me an example?" asked Andre.

Mr. Stiller replied, "Sure. The seminar I attended suggested designing a lead generation and prospecting process that creates a minimum of three positive touches—fusion points—prior to even asking for the first sales-conversation appointment. With each touch, add a brief note that lets the prospect know that you'll be reaching out and asks them to expect your call. My wife and I decided to sell the business before we could implement this concept into our sales model. But, I feel very confident that it would work well."

"What would you suggest on those contacts?" asked Andre.

"Be creative. Anything the potential client may find valuable will work. It may be something that's helpful for their business, a greeting card with a message they'd like, or possibly sending them a copy of an award or positive review they received about their business. It takes a little effort, but I'm confident the return on the time invested will be profitable."

Andre looked at his watch, then said, "You've given me a lot to think about. I'm sure I'll have more questions as things move forward. Would it be alright to keep meeting with you on occasion?"

"Absolutely, Andre. It'll be my pleasure."

Andre raised his eyebrows and said, "You just created a fusion point with me, didn't you? I see the logic in what I need to accomplish. And I'm having a very positive emotional response to your kindness in being willing to help me."

Mr. Stiller smiled. "That's right, Andre. And you created a fusion point with me too. Anytime I see a young leader who is still a student, wants to improve the lives of those in their business, and who is willing to listen, it's a very positive emotional experience for me as well."

The two men stood and shook hands.

Andre said, "Oh. By the way, Thaddeus Tucker said to tell you hello. I met with him this morning. I think I'll be bringing him on to my sales team."

Andre's comment brightened Mr. Stiller's eyes. "Thaddeus will be very green in sales. But he's also very bright. I'm glad to hear that you're doing that." He laughed. "He'll definitely try your patience at times. But he's a fine young man, and if you can teach, he can learn."

Andre replied, "I'm glad to hear you say that. I think I'm up to the challenge."

Mr. Stiller said, "I think you'll find that Thaddeus is as well."

7

I Thought This Would Be Easy

T haddeus savored the first sip of his morning coffee as he considered the events of the last few weeks.

Never thought I'd end up in sales. It's funny how life can change directions. I'd planned to teach music, and now I'm selling employee-benefit programs. Didn't see that coming!

Thaddeus never may have considered a position like this, but now, only a month later, he was pleased that he had. He was so excited after the initial interview that he had trouble sleeping that weekend. He'd called Andre at 8:00 a.m. on Monday morning and accepted the job. The earning potential was much better than his customer-service-manager position. He loved the idea that rather than being stuck in an office building all day, he could get out and make sales calls in the fresh air. And since the hot and humid days of New Orleans in August had now given way to the hot and humid days of New Orleans in September, he knew the more comfortable weather of fall was just around the corner.

He had completed his training and was now making sales calls in the area. Each insurance carrier had provided product training through a series of online classes and videos. Stencil, Osgood, and Broughton provided classroom training. Andre had also spent time in the field with Thaddeus and two other new salespeople—Lindsey and Lindsay–

51

–brother and sister twins with parents who apparently had a great sense of humor.

"Dad heard George Foreman being interviewed about his five sons, all of whom he named George," Lindsey had told Thaddeus. "So he named us Lindsey and Lindsay."

Lindsay had agreed. "That's right. That way, when he'd call out, 'Lindsay!' we'd both come to him."

The training equipped the new salespeople with strategies to identify and contact prospects, to set initial appointments with decision makers, and to have actual sales conversations. Overall, though inexperienced, Thaddeus was excited to go out and meet business owners in the area.

He believed he was ready.

Ready to make the contacts.

Ready to earn those great commissions.

Ready to go out into the New Orleans marketplace and break company sales records for his new employer.

Piece of cake, right?

Wrong!

It didn't work as easy as Thaddeus had expected, and a heavy dose of humility was headed his way.

Most of his attempts to set appointments with the decision makers were stopped before they began.

"I'm sorry. We already have employee benefits."

"I'm sorry. Ms. Kelley only sees salespeople with an appointment."

"I'm sorry. I'm sorry. I'm sorry."

I'm sorry, too. I thought this was going to be much easier. Salespeople mostly play golf and take customers to lunch, right?

Wrong again!

He remembered something Andre said. "Sales will either be the highest-paying hard work you'll ever do, or the lowest-paying easy work you'll ever do. It's important to understand that you can't make a six-figure income, only putting in minimum-wage effort."

Even when Thaddeus was able to make contact with an actual decision maker, he was getting objection after objection and struggled to get appointments scheduled for his sales presentations.

"We're not interested."

"But..."

"Your price is too high."

"But..."

"We already have that taken care of."

"But..."

Note to self. Starting a sentence with the word, "but" isn't much help in overcoming objections.

It was Friday afternoon, and Thaddeus had generated no sales this week. He actually hadn't even set a single appointment.

Somewhat because of the time of day, and somewhat because of the level of frustration he was feeling, he made the decision to stop making sales calls at 4:00 and have an early dinner at Rosario Boudreaux's.

As he walked up to the door, the host greeted him with a smile. "Welcome to Rosario Boudreaux's! How many today?"

"Just one," he said to the young lady, as he held up his index finger.

"Would you like to sit at the bar? It's full service."

"That'll be fine," replied Thaddeus.

The bar at Rosario Boudreaux's was gorgeous. It was artistically constructed of elegant mahogany that brought two words immediately to mind: beauty and culture. The woodwork had a French flair, and ornate carvings adorned the sides and columns. The chairs around the tables had an aged patina, and the bar stools coordinated perfectly. Tall interior walls made of old exposed brickwork confirmed that the building was at least a century old. And a mirror spanned the full length of the bar. The doors behind Thaddeus were open, and the mirror gave him an interesting view of the passersby on the street. It reminded him of watching a movie in a theater. But in this case, the performance was the street life of New Orleans.

The bartender was a tall man, well over six feet, who appeared to be in his late fifties, based on the color of his hair and the laugh-line wrinkles on his face. He said, "Good afternoon, young man! How are you today? I'm Terry, and I'll be taking care of you."

Thaddeus noticed the bartender's name tag. It bore the name *Tip* instead of Terry.

Is that his name, or is he subliminally planting the seed for my generosity? He chuckled at the thought.

"What's the story behind your name tag? Is *Tip* a nickname?"

Terry laughed and replied, "Good eyes! Not everyone's that observant."

He added, "It's a work nickname, I suppose. When I first began bartending, there was already another person behind the bar with the name Terry. So I began using the name *Tip* to help reduce the patrons' confusion. It started as a joke, but the name just stuck."

Thaddeus noticed an empty jar on the bar top labeled "Tip's Jar." Dropping a couple of bucks into the container, he said, "Well, it's working for you! Great marketing!"

Terry laughed and said, "That's what I thought, too. Although it backfired at my last job. After the first week, half of the waitstaff had changed their names to *Tip* as well."

Thaddeus laughed. "So, what did you do?"

Terry smiled. "I labeled my jar *Bigger Tip's Jar!*"

Both men laughed as Terry took Thaddeus's order back to the kitchen window.

Returning his eyes to the mirror—watching the cinema unfolding in the reflection before him—he noticed the young singer he had enjoyed listening to a month earlier. She walked through the doorway, pulling her equipment cart behind her.

She approached the bar, stood beside Thaddeus, but didn't take a seat.

Getting Terry's attention, she said, "Hi, Terry!"

"Hello, young lady! How's my favorite New Orleans busker doing today?"

"Doing quite well, sir! Thanks for asking. And you?"

"For a seventy-five-year-old man, I'm doing very well indeed! Thank you!"

Thaddeus gave Terry a confused look.

Terry said, "Well, if I'm going to lie about my age, I am going to say that I'm older than I really am. For fifty-eight, I look pretty good. But for seventy-five, I look great! I'm kind of a stud!"

Thaddeus laughed. Livia only grinned. It wasn't the first time she'd heard Terry make the comment.

Terry asked, "The usual, Livia? Hot ginger tea with a little cayenne pepper sprinkled on top?"

"Yes, sir. Thank you."

Thaddeus said, "Cayenne pepper in hot tea sounds really interesting! I put it in my coffee each morning."

Livia nodded.

Terry said, "Livia, this is Thaddeus. Thaddeus, this is Livia."

The two exchanged greetings as Terry walked back to the kitchen window.

"We actually met a month or so ago. You probably don't remember," said Thaddeus. "It was my first time hearing you. You're *really* good."

Livia blushed—just a little. "Thank you," she said, choosing to leave out the detail that she remembered him.

The server brought Thaddeus his salad and Livia her tea. It was his longtime friend, Martine.

"Hi, Thaddeus!" Martine said, giving him a hug and a smile.

"Hi, Livia!" she said, giving her the same. "So, you two know each other?"

"No. Not really," said Livia.

"Just officially met," added Thaddeus.

Martine said, "Two of my favorite people in one place? My lucky day! Livia, I've known Thaddeus since our school days. He's been a good friend. He was in a few weeks ago when you were singing. I bragged about you, and he stayed for a while." Putting her hand into the air for a fist-bump, she said, "His check went up and so did my tip! Thank you, Livia!"

Livia laughed and bumped. "Glad I could help!"

Thaddeus said, "You two are in cahoots, aren't you? Cahoots, I say!" He smiled, partly because of the levity of the moment, but mostly because *cahoots* wasn't a word he normally used. However, his mother had used it often. He didn't know which of his brain cells fired, producing one of his mother's favorite words. But he was glad they had.

"Thaddeus has a background in music, Livia," said Martine. "He even used to play on these streets a few years back."

"Well, I wasn't nearly as good as you, Livia. But I enjoyed it."

Livia asked, "Why'd you stop?"

Thaddeus didn't answer at first. He thought back about the time of his father's passing and his choice to drop out of college, get a job locally, and stay close to his mother.

"Life happened," he replied.

He added nothing.

Livia could tell that there was more to the story, but chose not to ask. She needed to get to the corner and set up. And from the look on his face, Thaddeus's story would take some time.

"Plus," Thaddeus added, "it got so embarrassing when all the girls would come up and flirt with me." With a bit of fake bravado, he said, "Yes. Everybody wants to date the tuba player."

Livia stifled a chuckle, and only nodded. She wasn't sure if laughing would be appropriate or disrespectful. So she kept her laughter inside.

Thaddeus said, "Seriously though. You're really talented and I enjoyed your music very much the last time I was here. You gave what began as a terrible day a much softer and kinder finish."

"Thank you," said Livia as she picked up her cup of tea from the bar top and headed towards the door. "Gotta go to work. Take care."

"Nice to meet you, Livia," said Thaddeus.

Martine's comments about Thaddeus had put Livia more at ease with him. She liked Martine and trusted her.

She looked back over her shoulder, gave him a smile and said, "We met… a month ago," then she turned and walked out the door.

Thaddeus's phone buzzed in his pocket. It was Andre.

"Good afternoon, Andre!"

"Hi Thaddeus! Just thought I'd touch base and see how your week's been."

"It's been a little rough, frankly. I didn't accomplish much. I made lots of attempts, but seemed to get shut down at every turn."

Andre replied, "Sorry things didn't go the way you wanted. Don't let it get you down too much. Some days are like that. Why don't you drop by the office on Monday morning, and we'll talk about what happened and how to handle things in the future."

"Will do. Thanks."

Andre said, "Oh, and make a list for me. Think about your week, the questions you asked, the responses you were given, and write them down…"

Thaddeus interrupted, "That part's easy. I didn't ask any questions. I just tried to tell them who I was, what we do, and tried to get an appointment with the decision maker."

Andre laughed. "That's good. Now I know where to spend my time. See you Monday."

Thaddeus finished his salad listening to Livia sing.

Was he tired? Sure.

Was he frustrated? Somewhat.

But he was also very excited to see what Andre had in store for Monday.

8

Changing Frames

Monday morning arrived, and Thaddeus was preparing for his meeting with Andre. He decided to fill a thermos with his special coffee blend, stop at Cafe du Monde to grab some beignets, and treat Andre to breakfast.

He sent a text.

> I'll bring in breakfast for us this morning.

In a few seconds, his phone buzzed.

> Sounds great. See you soon!

His morning drive took him past Jackson Square, a historic park in the heart of the French Quarter overlooking the Mississippi River. It was originally a public square and military parade ground. But now, for more than a century, it had been home to an open-air artists' colony where creators displayed their works on the square's iron fence. Thaddeus smiled as childhood memories of picnics there with his mother and father played through his mind.

His thoughts took him back to a time when his family was enjoying a lunch in the park. Thaddeus was only four years old. He couldn't remember why, but he'd been very fussy. A grumpy and sullen kid, apparently on a mission to spoil the day.

A woodpecker had rapidly tapped on a nearby tree. In an attempt to improve his disposition, his mother asked, "Thaddeus. Did you hear that woodpecker?"

Young Thaddeus listened with his arms folded and his face still frowning.

"No!"

The woodpecker repeated its rhythmic tapping.

Young Thaddeus said, "I didn't hear it that time, neither!"

If they wanted to have a good time, it's a wonder they ever took me with them anywhere!

After picking up the pastries, Thaddeus drove to the office, parked under the shade of a live oak tree, and walked into the building.

"Good morning, Henry!" Thaddeus said, setting a couple of beignets on the reception desk.

"Good morning, Thaddeus! Are those from Cafe du Monde?"

"They are!"

"Thank you! Much appreciated!"

Thaddeus replied, "My pleasure. Is Andre in yet?"

"Yes. He's in his office."

Thaddeus walked past the reception desk and down the hallway to Andre's office. Holding up the thermos and the bag of pastries, he said, "Food's here. Where would you like to meet?"

Andre looked up from his computer and smiled.

"Thanks! Let's meet in the conference room. We can grab a couple of plates, cups, and napkins from the break room along the way."

The two men entered the conference room and took the seats at the corner of the table. Andre arranged the plates and napkins while Thaddeus filled their cups.

Thaddeus said, "I'm looking forward to hearing what you think about my coffee recipe."

"I'm looking forward to trying it," replied Andre. "You've been telling us all we should give it a go!"

Andre lifted the cup and inhaled. The look on his face was not what Thaddeus expected. Instead of a pleasant look of anticipation, it was a wincing look of trepidation.

He took a sip.

His expression did not improve.

He crinkled his nose and said, "Interesting."

Even though he made no further comment about the brew, Thaddeus could tell that it wasn't Andre's favorite flavor combination.

A younger Thaddeus—even the version only a month younger—would have begun a debate about the merits of cayenne pepper and the flavor profile of chicory. However, the last thirty-three days had matured him somewhat.

Wow! My brain just stopped my mouth from taking over the moment! Jolie would be so proud!

He just smirked and said, "Want me to go grab you another cup from the break room?"

"No need. Let's get started. Did you make a list of the things you ran into last week?"

Thaddeus opened a note on his phone.

"Yes, I did."

Scrolling through the list, he said, "Mostly, I kept getting shut down before even getting to reach the business owner. It didn't seem to matter if I was on the phone or making contact in person. I struggled to get past the gatekeeper."

Andre made a note on his legal pad. "What else?"

"The rare times I actually spoke to the business owner, I struggled immediately. They didn't seem to have any interest in listening to what we have to offer. And I didn't know how to overcome their objections."

Andre scribbled. "Anything else?"

Thaddeus replied, "I thought I was well prepared. I knew my stuff. I expected good things to happen. But all the no's made it a pretty tough week."

He asked Andre, "Are you sure I can do this?"

Andre laid his pen on his pad and gave Thaddeus a look of confidence, comfort, and compassion. "Yes, I am. If you'll apply what I'll teach you, we can get you through this."

Andre's comments didn't surprise Thaddeus. He may have only known him a short while, but he already had great respect for him. If for no other reason, it was because of the type of leader Andre had chosen to become.

Andre began to teach.

"Thaddeus, the first principle I'm going to teach you is to *set a proper frame* with yourself, your prospects, and every person you'll meet in your sales process."

Pulling out a notepad, Thaddeus asked, "Frame?"

Andre replied, "Yes. I use the term *frame* to describe how each person views the events unfolding in front of them. How they see their world. Just like a picture or window frame, it's comprised of different pieces that create an opening to see what's in front of us. The direction of that frame has a definitive impact on our perspective."

Thaddeus wrote a single phrase on his notepad.

Set a Proper Frame

Andre said, "In relationships, both personal and business, that frame is constructed from pieces of our personal experience—our past. Those experiences determine how we react in most situations. That frame is solid. We can't change the materials it's made from anymore than we can change our past. But we *can* shift it from one view to another and change the perspective. When we change the perspective, we can change the response."

Thaddeus laughed and said, "I'll venture a guess that you had to do some serious resetting of that frame with Virginia, when you ran the idea of bringing me into your sales team past her."

Andre grinned. "No comment."

Continuing, Andre said, "It's like how I parent my children. When my three-year-old son falls down and skins his knee, I could react emotionally, rush over, pick him up, and make a big deal of it. What do you think his response would be?"

"Crying, I suppose," answered Thaddeus. "Pretty upset."

"Exactly. But if I control my own emotions first, I can reset his frame by walking over to check on him calmly, laugh just a little and say, 'That looked like fun.'"

Andre asked, "What do you think his response would be?"

Thaddeus thought for a second. "He'd probably laugh it off."

"Right again. Changing the frame changes the response."

"Okay," said Thaddeus, still looking confused. "How do we do that?"

Andre replied, "I'll teach you by taking you through a similar process, if that's okay with you."

Thaddeus nodded, "Absolutely! I'm ready."

Andre said, "From what you said, the no's you got last week frustrated you. And you're questioning your abilities to do the job, just a little. Is that correct?"

Thaddeus agreed.

Andre said, "I can see how that could be something worth considering. Especially after making so many contacts and getting such little results. And even though I've coached many newbies into becoming great salespeople, knowing that may not help change how you feel at this moment."

Thaddeus listened.

Andre said, "If I may, let me shift your perspective on sales just a bit. The word no isn't what drives people away from a sales career. What gives them pause is thinking that they're the only salesperson who gets a no. They see the award winners going across the stage and getting recognized at our meetings. Then they assume the superstar is much better than them. When that happens, they begin to think maybe they don't have what it takes."

Thaddeus kept quiet, but totally understood what Andre was saying. He'd felt exactly the same way.

Andre added, "But the truth is… even the superstars get a lot of nos in their work. They often get more than most. But they just keep going. They don't allow the lack of a sale to keep them from moving forward to their next call."

Thaddeus asked, "So, you're saying that if I get a lot of nos, I'm in good company?"

Andre replied, "Yes. In any sales career, getting a no is a normal part of the work. It's not unusual to get them more often than a yes. Most salespeople find that they have to pour through a gallon of nos to produce a quart of yeses."

Thaddeus wrote:

Set a Proper Frame—Yeses and Nos
1) Everyone gets nos.
2) A gallon of nos equals a quart of yeses.

Andre said, "Track your numbers so we can see if your results are below what they should be. Get really great at your skills. There's no excuse for not becoming excellent at your job. Then make the calls without worrying about the nos. Eventually, after you have enough data, we'll do a little fun math together. We'll divide your income by the total number of calls you've made. Then you'll be able to think about earnings per contact, rather than earnings per sale."

Thaddeus looked puzzled.

Andre added, "Nothing helped my attitude more, when prospecting, than knowing when I looked at the numbers—my average contact was worth fifty dollars to me. Instead of thinking that I made nothing on the fifteen who said no, and two-hundred dollars each on the five who said yes—I earned one-thousand dollars because I was willing to contact all twenty. That was an average of fifty dollars per contact—even when they said no."

Thaddeus quickly did the math in his head from his previous week's sales calls. He smiled and thought, *I hope my average is that good. That would be over five-thousand dollars!*

"If they said yes, it was great! But I didn't get super excited. Fifty bucks wasn't going to pay the mortgage. If they said no—great! Losing fifty bucks wasn't going to break me. If they said, 'The decision maker wasn't there'—great! If they said, 'We're happy with our current supplier'—great!"

Thaddeus began to understand. He scribbled on his pad.

Set a Proper Frame—Yeses and Nos

1) Everyone gets nos.
2) A gallon of nos equals a quart of yeses.
3) Get great at my skills.
4) Calculate my earnings per contact.

Andre said, "When I grasped that I earned my income because I was making a large number of contacts—each being worth fifty dollars to me based on my averages—my focus shifted and it became easier to detach from the results. And the idea of earning fifty dollars per contact inspired me to contact more prospects."

Thaddeus asked, "You reframed the whole thing, and it no longer seemed as frustrating?"

"Yes. It was still work. Hard work. But when I saw things framed from a different perspective, it was a pivotal moment for me."

"That makes sense." said Thaddeus.

Andre asked, "So you feel better about everything now, correct?"

Thaddeus thought for a few seconds, and replied, "Yes."

"That's because I reset the frame of how you see a no."

Andre thought for a moment, then continued. "I could have reacted based on my emotions. Here I have a new salesperson before me with tremendous potential. He's gotten some rejection and is doubting himself. I don't want him to quit."

Andre put his face down into his hands in feigned panic, and cried, "What do I do? What do I do?"

Thaddeus laughed.

"But instead, I reset the frame by doing four things. I controlled my own emotions and didn't rush over to pick you up when you *skinned your knees*. I asked questions to make sure that I understood your actual issue. I empathized with what you were feeling and then let you know I saw your concern as a valid consideration. Then, finally I shifted the frame so that you could see the word no from a different perspective."

Thaddeus wrote:

4 Steps to Reset a Frame:

1) Control my emotions.

2) Ask questions to ensure I understand.

3) Empathize.

4) Shift the frame to change the perspective.

"And I really do feel better about it," said Thaddeus.

Andre said, "You'll find the same process helps many areas of your sales model, especially when your goal is to become *ObjectionProof*."

"What do you mean?"

Andre replied, "Earlier, you mentioned you struggled to get past the *gatekeeper*. And your sense is that if you could gain their cooperation, you could move forward and reach the decision maker, right?"

"That's right."

"I get it. That's certainly something to consider. But what if we change the frame—change your view of what a *gatekeeper* actually is?"

Thaddeus sat up in his chair. "Go on."

"The administrative assistant's job is to protect the owner's time. If they allow everyone access, business owners can't get their work done. So, when they stop you, they're only doing their job. And we shouldn't get mad at anyone for just doing their job, right?"

With some hesitation, Thaddeus replied, "Right."

"But if you can get the *gatekeeper* on your side—if they become your ally instead of your adversary—they may be willing to help you. Your goal should be to transform them from the *gatekeeper* into the *keyholder*."

"Keyholder?" Asked Thaddeus.

"Yes. They control your access to the decision maker, just the same as a security guard controls access to a high-end jewelry store. The keyholder will often unlock the kingdom for you when they understand what's in it for them."

Thaddeus asked, "How do I do that?"

Andre replied, "Simple. Focus your phrases on the value to the *keyholder.* Point them toward how they'll personally benefit from taking the step you're asking them to take—helping you meet the decision maker."

Thaddeus thought for a second, then said, "Keep going."

"If the keyholder owns one of our products, and then has a medical situation arise where we would be of financial help, do they benefit?"

Thaddeus replied, "Yes. They do."

"That's right. But do the words you say when talking to them mention that? Or are you only asking them to give you access to the owner?"

Thaddeus thought for a few seconds. "Honestly, it's the latter, not the former. What I say is only asking for the appointment."

Andre nodded. "So change that. Don't ask for the appointment in order to make a sales presentation to the owner. Instead, consider asking for the keyholder's help in meeting the owner so you can help *the keyholder* have access to a program that gives them money for personal expenses when medical needs surprise them. They're *much* more likely to help you meet the owner when they see that you're wanting to help *them*."

Thaddeus shook his head, and said, "I'm not just saying this to curry favor with you, but that's genius! The gatekeeper can become my friend, the keyholder, if they see how they personally benefit from helping me."

"That's correct."

"Why didn't you teach this in training school?" he asked.

Andre laughed. "I did." He added, "But don't feel bad. That was a lot to learn. Training school is often like trying to take a sip of water from a fire hose."

Thaddeus laughed as he wrote again on his pad.

Turn the Gatekeeper into the Keyholder:

1) Stop asking for appointments to introduce our company to the decision maker.

2) Focus on resetting the frame by using phrases that point out how the person I'm speaking with personally benefits.

Andre said, "Often, in the midst of making sales calls, we can forget things. Give yourself permission to not be perfect. But keep improving."

Thaddeus nodded.

Andre said, "When you're speaking with the company owner, I want you to reframe *their* perception of what you're asking for as well. Many people seem to have a natural resistance to sales calls. So, stop asking for appointments where they can meet with a salesperson about employee benefits. Instead, invite them to spend a little time with you so that, together, you can find out if they may be able to take advantage of their value proposition."

Thaddeus asked, "What do you mean? Don't you mean *our* value proposition? I thought a value proposition was what we bring to the table."

Andre replied, "A common misperception. But that's not the reality of a value proposition."

Thaddeus had a puzzled look. "Explain, please."

Andre paused, then said, "Certainly. It's a mistake to ask for a sales appointment to present what we do. The decision maker actually doesn't care about that in most cases. They don't benefit by listening to how great our products are, how well we do our job, nor how wonderful a salesperson you are. They benefit from how *their* world gets better because they work with us."

Seeing the confused look on Thaddeus's face, Andre added. "In essence, the value proposition is *their* value from *our* proposition. So spend a little brain time to construct phrases you can use to focus their attention on how *they* benefit—and how their benefit begins with your invitation for a meeting."

Thaddeus nodded. "Can you give me an example?"

Andre replied, "Sure. If you ask for a few minutes to introduce them to our company, tell them what we do, and to show them how we can help, a small percentage of people will give you the meeting. However, if you *invite* them to spend a few minutes with you to see if you can improve their profit margin, reduce employee turnover, or reduce their payroll-taxes, a greater number will give you their time. So, when you really understand how *their* world gets better by giving you a few minutes, and you use phrases leading to that benefit, your success level rises."

Thaddeus added to his notes:

Set the frame with the decision maker:
1) Focus on *their* value from *our* proposition.
2) Invite them to spend a few minutes for their benefit.

Thaddeus said, "So, when I reframe the reason for the contact, and focus their thoughts toward their benefit, I change their perspective, which will often change the result."

"Exactly!"

Andre thought for a second, and said, "There's one last area where I'd like to reset your frame. It's from something you said earlier."

"What?"

"You said you didn't know how to *overcome their objections.*"

"Right."

"Thaddeus, I don't want you to overcome anyone's objections... ever."

"What?" Thaddeus asked. "Isn't that a mistake? If I don't overcome their objections, how can I make the sale?"

Andre smiled and asked, "Have you ever been overcome by anything? Maybe an illness? Maybe an argument?"

"Sure."

"Did you like that experience?"

"No. Not really."

Andre said, "Bingo! Nobody likes to be overcome by anything—or anyone. Sometimes, we don't mind being overcome *with* something, such as happiness, joy, or love. But, an objection is like an opinion. And nobody wants their opinion being overcome by the person visiting with them. Look no further than the political landscape to see an example of that point. In sales, if you're wasting time trying to overcome objections, it becomes a *'she said this, so I said that',* back-and-forth battle in which everyone loses."

Thaddeus paid close attention.

Andre said, "If a business owner tells you they already have insurance, don't debate them and try to overcome their point. Instead, take them through the same process I used with you—reset the frame and help them find a solution. Work within their objection."

Thaddeus raised an eyebrow and tilted his hands to the sky. "Example?"

70

Andre said, "Sure. For example, if they say they already have insurance, control your emotions, ask questions, empathize, and then reset the frame."

Andre paused, then added. "Don't panic and react to their statement. Instead, ask something like, 'So, if I'm understanding you correctly, you already have an employee-benefit program in place. Is that right?' Then listen to their answer. Make sure you understand. Follow that with something like, 'I understand, and that's certainly something to consider. While we've been honored to help other companies who already had benefit programs in place, this solution may not be the right fit for your organization.'"

Thaddeus asked, "Wouldn't that give them another reason to say no?"

Andre replied, "Oddly enough, the better you are at giving them an *out*, the less likely they are to take it."

Thaddeus said, "Alright."

"Then set the frame in a new direction with something like, 'What I really wanted to visit with you about is a way that we can increase your employee loyalty even greater than it already is. That reduces your turnover and training expenses. And we can often even reduce your payroll-taxes. Any money we save by doing that will go back onto your bottom-line profit."

Thaddeus said, "And we do that by having a full, rich benefit program in place that attracts and retains the employees, and by the tax savings we can generate in how we set up the payroll-deduction program, right?"

"Right." replied Andre.

Thaddeus wrote:

Don't try to Overcome Objections

Use 4 Steps to Reset a Frame to work within the objection:

1) Control my emotions.

2) Ask questions to insure I understand.

3) Empathize.
4) Shift the frame to change the perspective.

Andre said, "The last thing I'll suggest when you're talking with the final decision maker is to make it easy for them to say no."

Concerned, Thaddeus asked, "What? Don't I want the appointment?"

Andre replied, "Yes, you do. But making it easier for them to say no, actually makes it easier for them to say yes. Say something along the lines of, 'I can't promise you anything yet, because I'm not sure your company will meet the criteria, or if we'll be a good fit for you. But I'm one-hundred percent certain that you and I will be the two most qualified people to make that determination.' Then ask for your meeting."

Thaddeus exclaimed, "Hey! Wait, a minute. That sounds very similar to the words you used when setting up my interview!"

Andre smiled. "That's true. Recruiting and interviewing are very similar to a sales conversation. I knew that the only way I could determine if you had the potential I believed you to have, and that you could evaluate the opportunity properly for yourself, was if we sat down together. What did you feel when I asked that question?"

Thaddeus replied, "I felt like I wanted to sit down and find out for myself."

Andre nodded. "Yes, and that's what we want the decision makers to feel as well."

Thaddeus agreed.

Andre said, "Hey, I'd like for you to help me with an experiment. Are you interested?"

"Sure. What can I do to help?"

Andre replied, "Mr. Stiller taught me something, and I'd like for us to test it. I'm calling it *Priming the Prospecting Pump*. I'd like for you to pick twenty-five prospects. Do a little research on them. Then send the decision maker something of value, three times, over a period of just a few days."

"What type of value?" asked Thaddeus.

Andre replied, "It could be as simple as sending them a copy of a positive online review, an article that would be beneficial to them or their business, or dropping off a small gift of some sort. Don't ask for a meeting with these contacts. Instead, include a brief note that concludes with the phrase, 'I'd like to meet you soon. Please expect my call.'"

"Okay. But what's that supposed to accomplish?" asked Thaddeus.

Andre replied, "It creates a fusion point—a positive emotional response that you'll later connect with the logic of the value proposition—*their* value from *our* proposition. After the third touch, call or drop by. When you do, ask for the decision maker by name, and let the keyholder know you believe they'll be expecting your call."

Thaddeus said, "Alright. I can do that."

Andre replied, "Great! Please give me the results after you complete the project. I want to track the numbers."

He added, "Let's talk some more after you get some appointments booked. I'll spend some time teaching you how to reduce any objections you get in your actual sales conversations."

"Sounds good."

Andre said, "And, Thaddeus…"

"Yes."

"Go out there and sell something!"

Thaddeus laughed, stood up, and went out to conquer the world.

Well… maybe not the world. But at least his cubicle.

His cubicle today.

The world tomorrow.

9

Priming the Pump

Thaddeus was excited to get to his desk and apply what Andre had just taught him.

He decided exactly how he would "prime the prospecting pump" with three touches prior to asking for the first meeting with a prospect.

For the first touch, Thaddeus chose to go with a personalized recognition of the potential client's company. He looked at their website, online reviews, or mentions in the press for things that would inspire pride in their organization. By sending something praiseworthy, Thaddeus believed he would achieve the goal of creating a positive emotional response. He also believed that just this simple act would make him stand out from other salespeople attempting to make contact.

The second touch was an article he'd found online that detailed the top five reasons employees leave any company. The article described the true cost of employee turnover and how employee benefits play into their decision. He felt the article would be helpful whether the company became his client or not. He planned to email it to each prospect.

Even if they don't do business with me, maybe they'll start to see me as a helpful resource.

The third touch he chose was to send a greeting card, personalized for each decision maker. He found a service online where he could upload a personalized picture, type a note, and click send. The service would mail a tangible card to the recipient—a genuine piece of paper they could hold—sent by Thaddeus.

He selected twenty-five prospective companies from his database. He then invested the rest of his day doing online research, preparing each touch, and getting the initial emails ready. The first would go out that afternoon. The second touch would go out on Wednesday. And the third touch, the greeting cards, would go into the mail Tuesday. But with a couple of days for the mail to run, Thaddeus estimated they'd receive the card after the second touch.

With each touch, he included an appropriate phrase based on the item sent. He also added a comment that he planned to reach out soon, asking them to expect his call.

At the end of the day, Thaddeus was tired. He found himself thinking about how much work the process had involved. But then he remembered his coaching from Andre.

Wait a minute there, big boy! Reframe this! Last week, you spent five days making more than one-hundred contacts and got absolutely no results. Now you're putting in a bit of extra work today to implement a process that may bring you better results. If you get three to five new meetings with decision makers, you win!

The reframing worked. Thaddeus immediately felt less fatigued. He didn't have results to track yet, but he believed this process would be much more effective.

The next morning, Thaddeus spent about two hours getting the cards sent out to the prospects. Each had a simple message:

Hi Jazlyn,
I plan to get in touch with you sometime this week, or next, to extend an invitation to you. Please expect my call.
Thanks so very much!
Thaddeus Tucker

Since he had plenty of time left in his day and didn't need to do anything more with those first twenty-five contacts until Wednesday, he decided to make some prospecting calls with other companies who weren't on the new list.

I'll make some more calls and really focus on how the gatekeeper––scratch that, how the keyholder benefits from helping me get the meeting. I'll track both groups and see what happens.

He opened his database of New Orleans area companies and began to dial the phone.

On his first call, the receptionist answered on the second ring.

"Bakersfield Mortgage Company! My name is Danielle. How may I be of service to you today?"

Thaddeus caught himself feeling a little anxious inside. Fortunately, her cheery voice seemed to help. Taking a deep breath, he proceeded.

"Hi, Danielle! My name is Thaddeus Tucker, and I absolutely love how you answered the phone! I think I can actually hear you smile!"

She laughed and said, "Why, thank you!"

Thaddeus replied, "My pleasure!"

"So, Thaddeus Tucker, what's the answer? How may I help?"

"I'd like to get in touch with Barbara Akin, if you can help me out."

"About what?"

"I'd like to extend her an invitation to visit with me to see if a program my company offers, which can put money into *your* hands when you're missing work because of an accident or illness of yourself, your spouse or your children—while at the same time reducing the payroll tax expenses for the company—would be a good fit for Barbara."

Dannielle said, "She doesn't take sales calls unless you have an appointment."

Thaddeus said, "That's to be expected. After all, if she takes every call, how could she get any work done, right?"

"That's right. Plus, she's actually not here at the moment, anyway."

Thaddeus said, "Danielle, if our companies are a good match for each other, it could be a real benefit to you. You may have never missed work due to taking care of an ill spouse or child…"

"Actually, I have."

"I'm guessing that the money you would've received from us may have been a good thing, right?"

"We could've used it, for sure."

Thaddeus said, "Do you think you could help me get in touch with Barbara?"

The phone was silent for a few seconds.

"Danielle, are you there?"

"Shhh. I'm thinking."

Thaddeus smiled. *This is already an improvement over last week's contacts.*

"Okay," he said.

Danielle said, "She comes into the office an hour before we open. She's the only one here at that time. Unless she's busy, she answers the phone. Give her a call tomorrow morning around seven o'clock. I'll let her know you're going to call."

"Thank you so much, Danielle!"

"My pleasure!"

As he disconnected the call, Thaddeus thought, *Wow! That was easy. Maybe too easy. Surely they can't all go that well, right?*

He was correct. Not all of his morning calls went as perfectly as the first. He got nowhere many times. However, he noticed a definite difference in the responses he was getting. Partly, he surmised, because of the phrases he was using. Somewhat, because his skill level was improving with each attempt. But Thaddeus believed the most likely reason for the change in results was how *he* felt about what he was doing. Reframing his perception of a gatekeeper into a keyholder didn't just transform them.

It transformed Thaddeus.

Before—even though he'd hoped for their aid—he actually viewed them as somewhat of an impediment to his forward progress. Now, he considered the person on the other end of the phone as someone he may be able to help, and if they saw that too, they may be more willing to assist him.

By mid-afternoon, Thaddeus had made twenty-five contacts. He believed the keyholder was going to help him in ten different cases. He even got through to one decision maker and was able to schedule a meeting.

That visit was scheduled with the human-resources director for a local commercial builder. It almost startled him when the keyholder put the call through. He didn't feel he'd done a great job with what he'd said. But, even though it wasn't perfect, it worked.

"This is Jessica."

"Hi, Jessica. I'm Thaddeus Tucker with Stencil, Osgood, and Broughton. Thanks so much for taking my call."

"My pleasure."

"The reason I'm calling is that I'd like to extend you an invitation for us to visit for about twenty minutes next week."

"What about?"

"A program our company has that's designed to increase employee loyalty even greater than it already is by helping *you* protect *their* income when they're missing work because of an accident or illness in the family. At the same time, the program potentially reduces your company's training and payroll-tax expense."

He added, "I can't promise you anything yet because I'm not certain that this will be a good fit for your company and ours, but I'm one hundred percent certain that you and I would be the two best people to make that determination, and we should be able to do so in just a few minutes.

"I'm going to be in your area next Tuesday afternoon and Wednesday morning. Would you have a twenty-minute opening on your calendar for us to meet?"

For a few seconds, she didn't speak.

Thaddeus got nervous.

Finally, she replied, "Let's see. I can work you in on Wednesday afternoon at two o'clock. Does that work for you?"

"It does."

"Okay. I look forward to meeting you, Mr. Tucker."

"Likewise, ma'am. Thank you."

As Thaddeus disconnected the call, he thought he was going to hyperventilate. It was exhilarating! He immediately walked down the hall to tell Andre about his results.

After listening to the details of Thaddeus's morning, Andre laughed and said, "That's great! Nice job!"

Andre added, "You'll get a lot of positive results when you do as I've taught you. But be ready. You'll still get a lot of nos as well. Remember, a gallon of nos for a quart of yeses."

Thaddeus nodded. "That's okay. I make money on every contact I make. And I can't wait to see how much that is!"

Thaddeus decided to leave his car at the office and take the St. Charles Streetcar Line to Rosario Boudreaux's to have a late lunch.

I wonder if Livia will be singing today?

The St. Charles Streetcar Line traveled past Tulane University and on to Canal Street. From there, Rosario's was just a few blocks away and when the weather is cooperative, a very nice walk.

Riding streetcars was one of Thaddeus's favorite experiences in New Orleans. They added such great flavor to the city. Of course, using the transit system and avoiding driving in the heavy traffic of the downtown business district was a definite stress reducer. And yes, one less car adding to the pollution in the area was something that made him feel he was being a good citizen. Also, being seated in a comfortable chair while someone else negotiated the route gave him time to answer emails and catch up on work.

But those things weren't what inspired his affection for this old form of transportation.

Thaddeus's love affair with the streetcars began during his childhood, when he and his parents would ride them through the city on Saturday mornings, attending to family errands. His father would keep him spellbound with tales of the historical significance of various landmarks along the route. Cemeteries, haunted houses, and famous mansions filled the city, as well as young Thaddeus's imagination.

He remembered his father saying, "Thaddeus, the St. Charles Streetcar Line is the oldest continuously running streetcar in the world." Then, with a smile of great pride in his city, he said, "It's one of only two streetcars listed as a National Historic Landmark."

As Thaddeus stepped up into the car and took a seat, the memory made him smile.

Dad, you'd have been great on any trivia show, as long as all the questions were about NOLA.

Boarding the St. Charles Streetcar was like stepping back in time to the 19th century. The cars were painted pea green with red trim around the doors and windows. The seats were assembled by hand with alternating light and dark wooden slats. And a cable for signaling the driver was carefully passed through eye bolts, draped in front of the canvas blinds, running along each side of the car. The dip of the cable between each eye bolt reminded Thaddeus of the smiley emoji he used on his phone.

Except for the video monitor above the windshield, giving passengers the details of the upcoming stops, a rider may never know they were living in modern times.

That monitor now chimed and told Thaddeus that his Canal Street stop was coming up next.

Thaddeus enjoyed walking through the French Quarter. The streets were worn with time and hurricanes. Most of the buildings were two to four stories tall. They displayed ornate Creole and Spanish-style balconies and trellises, and were well over one-hundred years old. He imagined the days when couples would stand on their balconies, men smoking fine cigars and women fanning themselves in the heat, as they waved at friends passing by.

And of course, his personal favorite, the buskers—New Orleans's greatest treasures, in his opinion—entertained the crowds.

He smiled as he approached Rosario Boudreaux's. A sizable crowd had already gathered around Livia as she was telling them a story, still sitting on the corner wall.

"This next song is an original," she said. "I wrote it during my first year of performing… uh…" she gestured to her surroundings, laughed and said, *"professionally?"*

The crowd chuckled with her. Not to belittle her status as a street performer, but because she had such a sweet sense of humor and a humble spirit. Livia had a natural ability to connect with the crowd. They loved her.

She continued, "I was just getting started and trying to explore new things. Trying to be courageous. Making mistakes…" Then laughing, she said, "and even learning from a few of them." Shaking her head, she admitted, "Not all—but a few."

She didn't just hold the crowd's attention, she held their hearts in the palm of her hand.

"It means a lot to me. I hope you'll like it too."

Livia began to sing a soft and slow jazz tune, which was made even richer by the sound of her lyrical and mysterious alto voice.

~ ~ ~*Livia's Song*~ ~ ~

Sittin' in the heart of my dreams.
Wrapped in the ghosts of music all around.
The chords are rich, the melodies seem
Filled with the soul I've found.

~

Eyes that only see me smile.

82

Ears that only hear the music in the air.
Lips that touch, swaying with style,
Dancing in the street without care.

~

I wonder if they'd stay,
Or go along their way,
If they could see inside,
This fear I try to hide,
They tell me that I'm more
Than I've ever been before.
"I just need to believe."

~

Believe in me?
Seems like such an easy thing.
Just make the choice.
Then rejoice.
Shine your star for all to see.

~

Believe in me?
But I see all my flaws.
Can I make the choice?
Overcome the little voice
That whispers "There's no 'believe' in me."

~ ~ ~

As Livia sang, many in the crowd had gotten their smartphones out and were sharing a live video on their social-media stream. When she finished, the applause was heartfelt and generous.

"Thank you, everyone, for your smiles, your videos, and your applause—oh, and yes, your tips," she chuckled, "They are all so very appreciated. I'm going to take a little break and be back in about twenty minutes."

After some minimal packing up of her equipment, which couldn't be left on the street while taking her breaks, she walked over to the restaurant, just as Thaddeus arrived at the door.

Opening the door for her, he said, "Livia, that was incredible. The words... the music... just beautiful. You pulled me right into the story with you. I loved it."

"Thank you, Thaddeus. Both for the compliment and the door." She smiled and walked inside.

"My pleasure!"

Thaddeus said, "The crowd was really enjoying you too! I'll bet those videos go viral. Do you have any recordings for sale?"

"No. That would require a bit of studio time." Smiling, she said, "They don't exactly give that stuff away."

"What about a record label? Have you ever pursued a contract with any of the local companies?"

Her eyes dropped, and her smile dimmed a little.

"Yes. But it didn't work out."

Thaddeus wanted to ask more questions to get the complete story. However, the change in Livia's demeanor gave him pause.

Maybe I'll ask more when we get to know each other better.

"Well, that's a shame. Their poor judgment is keeping the world from a wonderful artistic experience."

"That's very kind of you to say."

"I mean it. But now that I think of it, I may be wrong."

Livia looked surprised, but said nothing.

Responding to her expression, Thaddeus said, "The world may actually be getting that experience as the crowd gathers around you and films. I'll bet your videos are getting a lot of play—spreading, like kudzu. So the world may indeed be enjoying the *#lovingliviainNOLA* experience. Now we just need to see about getting you paid for it."

Thaddeus asked, "Have time for lunch? My treat."

"Thank you, but I can't. I'm only taking a quick break, and I have a few calls to make."

There were no calls to make.

There was no rush.

But there was also no comfort with Thaddeus yet. At least not enough for her to accept his invitation.

"No worries."

Livia lifted her phone and called her mother as she walked over to the host's stand. Thaddeus took a seat at the bar.

"Hello, Bigger Tip!" he said as the towering mixologist approached. "How's it going?"

"Hi Thaddeus!" replied Tip. "The day started off great, but then took a strange turn toward the weird."

"Weird? In New Orleans? Surely, you jest!"

Both men laughed.

"So what happened?" Thaddeus asked.

Tip answered, "Earlier today, a disheveled older man came in. He was thirty-ish pounds overweight. Seemed disoriented. He'd lost most of his hair. And there, on top of his head, was a large bullfrog."

Thaddeus nodded in agreement, grinned and asked, "A bullfrog? On top of his head? That *is* weird, isn't it?"

Tip replied, "It certainly is. Of course, this being New Orleans, it isn't unusual to see strange things. Freaky's the rule, not the exception. After all, we even have a voodoo museum! And them voodoo princesses can put their *voodoo hoodoo* on you, if ya know what I mean."

Thaddeus nodded, his smile growing. He asked, "Still. A frog on top of a man's head is pretty far out there, don't you think? Even here in New Orleans?"

"It is. But that's not the craziest part."

"It's not?"

"No."

"Well what, pray tell, is the craziest part?"

"I'm glad you asked. I'll tell you."

Tip raised both hands, questioning. "I asked him, 'How the heck did this happen to you?'"

"What did he say?"

"The man said nothing. But the frog croaked, 'Well, it all started as a wart on my ass!'"

Thaddeus laughed.

Tip said, "A talking frog is weird, right?"

"It is, indeed," said Thaddeus, still chuckling.

A server brought Thaddeus his salad as Livia walked past.

"Good to see you, Thaddeus."

"You too, Livia," he said with a nod.

Thaddeus finished his lunch as Livia mesmerized the crowd once again. Different people. Different songs. But the same enchanting voice.

He paid his check and began his walk back to Canal Street for his return streetcar ride.

As he walked, he noticed several small companies along the route. Realizing that he had some time to kill, he remembered an old saying his father loved. "Thaddeus, if you're going to kill time, try workin' it to death, son."

With a smile on his face, and a warm memory of his father in his heart, he decided to stop in a couple of businesses to gather information and see what happened. An unannounced sales call wasn't their normal strategy, and he realized it may not be the most effective way to start the conversation. But what did he have to lose?

It's better than making no calls. Who knows? I may set an appointment. And even if it's only one, that's a HUGE increase over none.

His focus was the same as it had been on the phone. He used phrases that helped the keyholder see how they benefited from helping Thaddeus meet the decision maker. Twice, he actually got to meet the business owner and scheduled appointments with both for the following week.

Wow! When I'm focused on how I can bring value to whomever I'm speaking with at the time, their response is so much more positive than what I experienced last week. I can't wait to tell Andre!

Receive Bob's Daily Impact Emails

Enjoy a dose of morning inspiration to power up your day, including thoughts on sales, leadership, communication, and more!

You can view a sample issue and, if you'd like, subscribe at:

http://burg.com/daily-impact

10

#lovingLiviainNOLA

L ivia took the evening off and spent it at home. If it had been a weekend, she couldn't have done so. The crowds would be too large to pass up. More people equaled more tips. But tonight, she was getting a little extra time with her parents.

"You're home early tonight, baby." Her mother smiled as Livia walked through the door. Giving her a kiss on the cheek, her mother said, "Good. I'll set another plate on the dinner table."

"Thank you," Livia replied, giving her mother a tight hug. "I'm pretty hungry. I skipped lunch."

Livia took her equipment to her bedroom and considered what Thaddeus had said.

I wonder how much those #lovingliviainNola videos are getting watched.

She opened her laptop and turned it on. Once the system had booted, she opened her browser and typed *#lovingliviainNola* into the search bar. She hesitated before hitting the enter key.

Why am I so nervous about seeing the results?

Would there be anything showing up in the search? She didn't know. The thoughts of finding out made her uneasy. But the thoughts of not knowing were also unpleasant.

She decided that not knowing was worse.

She inhaled slowly, held her breath, and clicked the enter key.

To her surprise, there were numerous pages of search results displaying on her screen, all with the hashtag, *#lovingliviainNola*.

As she scanned the links, she saw hundreds of people posting videos of her performances. There were posts from tourists around the world.

The videos were getting shared—and reshared—numerous times.

There weren't just a few people seeing her videos. There were thousands.

Tens of thousands.

Hundreds of thousands.

Wow! I had no idea.

When she walked back into the dining room, her father was already there.

Excited to see his daughter, he said, "Hey! How's my boonoonoonoos? Were doze tourists good to my baby today?"

Livia laughed. "Yes, Daddy. They were good to your baby."

He grabbed her and gave her a hug. "They'd better be. Otherwise, I'd have to come down there and open up a can of whoop-ass…"

Livia's mother cleared her throat and gave a stern look to Livia's father.

He laughed. "Alright, alright. I'll watch my language." Switching to a very imperfect attempt at a British accent, he said, "I meant to say I'd have to come down there and ask them, *ever so politely,* to please be kind to my baby girl."

They all laughed and sat down for dinner.

Looking at his wife, Livia's father asked, "How was your day, babe?"

"It was fine. Grandma called today. We're getting a new choir director at church."

Livia's father asked, "The Blackthornes are moving?"

"They are. Elizabeth got a job transfer to Dallas."

Livia was distracted. Her father noticed she was barely taking part in the evening's conversation.

He looked at her, and said, "I can't believe the news that the New Orleans City Council passed an ordinance requiring buskers to pay five-thousand dollars per year for a *license* to perform."

Her mother looked at him with a puzzled look.

"What do you think about that, Livia?" he asked, nodding his head in affirmation.

Coming out of her thoughts for a moment, but having no clue what had just been said, she replied, "Sounds good."

Her dad laughed. "Okay, baby. What's on your mind? You're obviously somewhere else."

Paying more attention now, she said, "I'm sorry. I was just thinking about something a friend said today. Actually, he's more of an acquaintance at this point. He asked me if I'd ever tried to sell recordings, or approached a label about signing me."

Her parents' expressions revealed their thoughts. They remembered Livia's previous experience with a potential record label. Most businesses try to be honest and upfront. They know that taking great care of their customers and workers is the right way to build their company. Record labels are no different. But there are also those that are less than honorable.

Livia had encountered one of those *less than honorable* record producers.

The table was quiet for a few seconds.

Finally, her mother spoke up.

"Livia, honey, companies are neither good nor bad. They are just companies, not people. When those companies are run by good people, they do good things. When they're run by bad people, they do bad things. But that doesn't mean that they're all bad."

"That's right, Livia," her father added. "One bad habañero pepper may ruin the jerk sauce at one chicken joint, but that doesn't mean they're all bad."

"Well, *that* jerk was bad, for sure," said Livia.

"True," said her mom. "But there have to be others who are good too."

During Livia's first year of busking, a man who said he loved her singing approached her and promised her the moon. Unfortunately, his promises were fake. What he really wanted was to get new and struggling performers to sign contracts with him, guaranteeing to make big things happen for them. However, before the ink on their signatures was even dry, he replaced those *guarantees* with requests for money to cover the expenses.

It took Livia a few months to realize that the man was taking advantage of her, and to get out of the contract. The entire experience left her with a natural distrust of recording execs, and thoughts of trying again were unsettling.

"Who is this *friend?* Do you know him well?" asked her father.

Livia replied, "No. I don't know him well yet. But he's not in the business at all. He was just asking."

Her parents relaxed a bit.

She continued, "He made a comment when he saw all the people recording me live to their social-media pages. He said something about the possibility of the videos going viral. It got me curious, so I checked just before dinner."

"What did you find?" asked her mom.

"Well... they're getting a lot of play."

Her dad asked, "What's a lot?"

Her eyebrows raised, showing her surprise.

"Over two hundred thousand views, from what I just saw."

"Whooo!" exclaimed her father. "I'd say dat's a lot, for sure!"

"It's gotten me to consider trying again."

"I think you should, baby," said her mother.

"Me too, boonoonoonoos.*"

Livia smiled and said, "No promises. Just thinking."

In her heart, she really wanted to try again. But in her stomach, where her fear seemed to dwell the most, there was so much doubt.

"Something to think about, definitely," said her father. "You can do anything, Livia. Keep getting better at what you do. Keep making fun things happen for the crowds. Believe in yourself. Then out-work everyone else." Then, with a mischievous grin, he said, "You'll kick a…"

"Again?" her mother scolded.

He looked at his bride with mischief in his eyes. "Sometimes, I just like to see if you're paying attention."

Looking back to his daughter, with an adoring look, he said quietly, "You really can do anything. Give it a shot." Then, whispering, he said, "You really will kick ass!"

11

Their Words—Not Yours

On Tuesday morning, Thaddeus got to work early. He was excited to update Andre about his Monday sales calls. After grabbing a cup of coffee from the break room, he walked over to Andre's office, tapped on the door frame and asked, "Got a few minutes?"

"I sure do!" replied Andre, as he walked over to his small circular conference table and gestured to the chairs. "Have a seat."

Thaddeus sat down.

"I had a fun day yesterday!" Thaddeus began.

"Can't wait to hear about it!" replied Andre.

Thaddeus recounted the results from the previous day's activities as Andre jotted notes down on a pad.

When Thaddeus finished, he said, "I've got three separate meetings booked with the decision makers next week. I'd like to get your thoughts and any pointers to help me prepare."

Andre nodded. "First, let me say great job! It's obvious that you're working on implementing what I've been teaching you. I appreciate that. But more importantly, those things will help you succeed at a higher level and get you there faster. So, nice work!"

"Thank you!"

"My pleasure." Looking down at his notes, Andre said, "You mentioned that you have two presentations with business owners and one with a human-resource manager, right?"

"That's correct."

"Okay. That actually means you probably have meetings with two decision makers and one decision influencer."

"Decision influencer?" asked Thaddeus.

"Yes. The human-resource manager, at least from my experience, is probably not the final decision maker. Instead, they'll be a person who gathers the information, and then makes a recommendation to someone else. They may not make the decision, but have no doubt, they will certainly influence that decision."

Thaddeus asked, "Should I handle that meeting differently?"

"Yes. Somewhat, anyway."

"How?" asked Thaddeus.

Andre replied, "Much sales training teaches that you shouldn't make presentations to non-decision makers. Some even go so far as to say that if you find your meeting is scheduled with someone who can't make the decision, you should reschedule the meeting to a time when the final decision maker may attend. While that may be sound advice in some cases, I don't think that's a hard-and-fast rule."

Thaddeus was puzzled. "Why?"

Andre replied, "With larger companies, there are often multiple steps to navigate in their corporate structure. Anything that appears to be hesitancy on your part to work within their structure would likely give the impression that you are being disrespectful to the person you're meeting with. That would hurt your efforts."

"Makes sense," said Thaddeus.

"Thaddeus, remember that a decision influencer may not be able to say yes to you. But they can definitely say no and block your forward progress."

Thaddeus asked, "Got it. So what do you recommend?"

Andre replied, "I'm sure you remember in your sales training, I taught you that your sales conversation, or presentation, has five parts."

"Yes, I remember. First is the rapport section, where I'll mainly focus on quickly establishing a relationship. Then comes the discovery section, where I'll ask questions, looking for their specific needs."

"That's right." said Andre.

"Next is the recommendation phase, where I'll make suggestions as to how we'll take care of the needs they mentioned. Then it's the credibility section, where I'll introduce our company and give testimonials from some of our clients."

"Very good," said Andre. "But that's only four. Do you remember the fifth?"

Thaddeus squinted his eyes slightly, and thought.

Shaking his head, he said, "I'm drawing a blank."

Andre laughed. "The fifth part is the close. Don't forget to ask them to do business with us."

Thaddeus laughed as well. "That would be helpful, wouldn't it?"

"Yes. It would."

Andre added, "When you're presenting to a decision influencer, it's best to add a couple of things to your rapport section and make a couple of adjustments to your close."

"How so?"

"In your rapport section, add two questions. First, ask them, 'Aside from you, who else will be involved in the decision-making process?' And if they give you a name, ask if it would be possible to include them in the meeting since that person may have questions that differ from the decision influencer's."

"Okay," said Thaddeus.

"If the final decision maker can join the meeting, great. If not, continue with the same sales conversation, but change your closing question."

Thaddeus asked, "What would you change?"

Andre said, "When you're closing the sale with a decision influencer, use four easy steps. First, take them off the hook. Second, give them a promotion. Third, ask your closing question. And fourth, go to work for them."

Thaddeus wrote on his notepad:

Closing with a Decision Influencer
1) Take them off the hook.
2) Give them a promotion.
3) Ask a closing question.
4) Go to work for them.

Thaddeus smiled. "Okay. I know you, Andre. You're about to give me an amazing example of doing exactly that now, right?"

Andre laughed. "How'd you know?"

"Lucky guess," replied Thaddeus.

"Let's roleplay it," said Andre. "You'll be the human-resource manager."

Thaddeus said, "Let's do it."

Andre said, "*Step one: take them off the hook.* Thaddeus, I already know from what you said earlier that you'll need to take this decision up the company hierarchy. But, with your permission, I'd like to ask you a question, anyway. And please feel completely welcome to tell me 'no,' if that's the right answer for you. Fair enough?"

Thaddeus replied, "Sure."

"*Step two: Give them a promotion.* I'm giving you a promotion. You're now the company owner." He laughed. "But don't get too excited. Imaginary promotions come with only imaginary raises as well."

Thaddeus laughed.

Andre went on. "*Step three: ask your closing question.* If the final decision were in fact yours, and yours alone, do you see any reason you wouldn't want to move forward with my recommendations?"

Thaddeus said nothing. Andre raised an eyebrow and gave a questioning look.

Thaddeus got the point. "Yes. I mean, no. I see no reason."

Andre said, "As a side note, you definitely want to wait for their reply. If they have an objection, that's been on their mind but not expressed, it usually comes out at that point."

"Makes sense," said Thaddeus.

Andre said, "*Step four: go to work for them.* Then I'd like to go to work for you. Rather than you learning all the things involved in what I've shown you, I'll be glad to come in and have this same discussion with you and the other people involved, without obligation on anyone's part. That should make things much easier for you, and I'll be able to answer any questions they may have. Then, if I need to leave the meeting, so that discussions may flow freely, I'll do so. Fair enough?"

Thaddeus replied, "It is."

Andre said, "Then ask to get that meeting on the calendar, even if only a tentative date, while you're there."

"I like that!" said Thaddeus. "What other helpful bits of wisdom can you impart to me today?"

Andre thought for a few seconds and said, "Each part of the sales conversation is important. Without building rapport, the prospect doesn't get the chance to feel comfortable with you. Leaving out the discovery puts you flying blind and you'll likely miss the mark on what they would find most valuable. Without recommendations, you can't provide solutions for them. And unless you establish our credibility, they won't feel comfortable saying yes."

Thaddeus laughed and said, "And if I don't close, they'll have to figure out how to do the paperwork all by themselves!"

"True," laughed Andre.

Thaddeus added, "And then I need to be ready to work with any objections I hear."

Andre nodded, then said, "The most important part of your sales conversation is the discovery section. The better *your* discovery, the fewer *their* objections. So, you want to plan your questions so that your prospect will comfortably open up and discuss their needs with you."

Thaddeus asked, "What kind of questions do you recommend?"

Andre said, "Use open-ended questions which can't be answered with a simple yes or no. Your goal is to gain insight into their needs from *their* perspective, not your own. The better your questions, the more effective you'll be in recommending the right solutions for their specific situation."

Andre paused for a moment, then added, "If you ask the right questions, and listen carefully, you'll often find that your prospect will actually say exactly what they need to hear."

Thaddeus asked, "What do you mean—*they'll* say what *they* need to hear?"

Andre replied, "It's simple. They really need to hear what their needs are, so that they can gain clarity on their issues. They also need to hear why those needs are important and how valuable a solution would be. But, Thaddeus, they need to hear those words coming from their own mouth. Not yours."

Thaddeus said with a chuckle, "But I like telling people what they need to do."

"Yes, you do," replied Andre. "However, in this case, your goal should be to ask questions that guide them to think through their issues, get them to discuss those points with you, and then arrive at a specific need for which our company offers a solution."

Thaddeus thought for a second, and said, "This is something I really need to work on. It's not my default setting."

"I understand. It's that way for many people. However, think about this. You could just tell them what you think they need. After all, you know what we do and how it specifically provides a great value to them…"

Thaddeus laughed. "I know! That's what I'm good at! Telling people what to do is my spiritual gift!"

Andre laughed too. "I've seen salespeople do that. But it's not very effective."

"Why not?"

Andre said, "Multiple reasons. One is that you should never assume you know what's important to your prospect until they tell you. Yes, you know why our programs would be great for their company. But if you don't ask questions, they won't discuss their priorities, and you'll miss things that are important to them. Ask questions that move them toward what we do. But do so with a mindset that acknowledges that you don't know everything and you want to learn."

Andre took a serious tone, and said, "There's another very big reason you should ask and listen, more than you show and talk. At this stage, they often haven't had a chance to get to know you, like you, or trust you—yet. So, as the salesperson, what you say may not be taken at face value. But if you ask great questions and they open up about the challenges they're facing, they'll become more convinced of their needs, and you'll become more accurate with your recommendations."

Thaddeus nodded.

Andre added, "Remember, when it comes to their needs, if you say it—it's debatable. But if they say it, it's the gospel truth."

Thaddeus said, "So, my job is to ask great questions so my prospect will say... what my prospect needs to hear?"

Andre replied, "Correct. And when you do this, you'll also create a bond with them. They'll see you as being genuinely interested in what their challenges may be. You'll be seen as a source for a potential solution. They'll like how that feels, and it'll be mentally easier for them to grant you permission to make your recommendations. Then, if they logically see that your recommendations will solve the challenges they've told you about, they'll feel much more comfortable moving forward with you."

Thaddeus said, "That sounds like a fusion point. You're connecting a positive emotional response to the logic of our solution."

Andre smiled and said, "You know, I hadn't realized that. But that's exactly why this structure works so well. The neurology of the brain makes them more at ease moving forward because of the combination of logic and positive emotion."

Thaddeus asked, "Do you have some favorite questions you've used before?"

Andre replied, "I do. But I'd rather see you come up with your own. Just remember, your inquiries need to generate discussion rather than one-word responses."

"Okay," said Thaddeus.

Andre said, "Why don't you go back to your desk and spend a little time developing your own questions? When you finish, bring them back and I'll take a look. A great place to begin is to list what *their* value is from *our* proposition. Then craft questions that will guide the discussion into some of those areas."

"Will do," said Thaddeus as he stood. "Be back soon."

Thaddeus returned to his desk, booted his computer, and began his list. At the top, he typed four different benefits, which he believed best described *their* value from *his* proposition.

Their Value From Our Proposition

1) Great employee benefits reduce turnover, which saves the company money on training expenses. Reduced expenses equals higher profits.

2) Great employee benefits make it easier to compete when hiring new employees. Better employees equals higher productivity and higher profits.

3) We offer many of our programs through payroll deduction, giving the company a way to add benefits without increasing their expenses.

4) The payroll deductions can reduce the employer's payroll-taxes. That increases bottom-line profits.

Okay, now what questions can I ask to generate a discussion resulting in them saying that these things are important to them?

~ ~ ~

After about an hour, Thaddeus returned to Andre's office.

"Got time to check my homework?" Thaddeus asked with a laugh.

"I do," replied Andre.

The two men returned to the small, round conference table.

Andre reviewed the page.

"I like how you've targeted your focus. What questions have you crafted?"

Thaddeus replied, "I've come up with three. First: 'For many companies, employee turnover has become a big issue over the last few years, and hiring great people seems more difficult. How are those things affecting you here?' Followed up with, 'What are you doing to offset those issues?'"

Andre nodded. "Not bad... shouldn't be a simple one-word answer. I can see that leading to a discussion of how they use their employee-benefit package to offset both issues."

Thaddeus moved on to his next question, "How would you feel— being able to offer a more full benefit package, if it created no extra expense for your company, and generated a reduction of payroll-taxes?"

Andre said, "Hmm...that one's pretty good. You may want to tweak it a bit. Experiment with it a few times and see what responses you hear. I find that questions including the phrase, 'How would you feel...' are usually best as follow-up questions. For me, anyway, they don't seem to work very well at discovering the underlying issues."

Thaddeus asked, "What do you mean?"

Andre replied, "If I were going to draw the conversation toward the fact that employers can offer many of our plans at no cost, I might try something like this. 'Are there employee-benefit programs you've

103

wanted to offer before, but chose not to do so?' Then follow that up with, 'Would you mind sharing with me what they were, why you felt it was important to offer them, and the reason you didn't move forward?'"

Thaddeus nodded. "I can see that working. I'd think most would say yes. And the reason they'd give for not going ahead would be because of the expense. That gives me the ability to solve the problem with a similar benefit through payroll deduction."

Andre said, "Then, as a follow up, I might ask how it would make them feel to be able to offer that program to the employees now, when budget concerns stopped them before."

"I see," said Thaddeus.

He looked down at his list. "My last question is pretty simple. 'Why do you offer employee benefits?'"

Andre replied, "Thaddeus, on one hand, that's a great question. You really want your prospect to think through their reasons for offering benefits. After all, everything we do will help, whatever their goals may be. That being said, as I've used that question in the past, the decision maker almost perceived it as too obvious. From their perspective, it was almost silly that I would ask. The answer, at least in their eyes, seemed a bit rhetorical."

"So, what'd you do?"

"I adapted."

"How so?"

"I learned I could ask a question with an obvious answer if I framed it properly."

"How'd you frame it?" asked Thaddeus.

Andre replied, "I said, 'With profit margins getting thin over the last few years, it's forced many employers to make some tough budget decisions. Some have reduced benefits. Others have cut them out completely. Yet, you still offer a nice package. I commend you for that. Do you mind if I ask why employee benefits are still important to you? Why do you go to the expense and the trouble?'"

"Did it work?" asked Thaddeus.

"It did. I was giving them an honest and heartfelt compliment, which they appreciated. And then I gave them time to tell me why it was important."

Thaddeus said, "Your prospect then said what your prospect needed to hear, right?"

"That's right," said Andre.

He added, "As they answer your questions, you're looking for them to mention two to four specific needs—needs for which we may provide value and help them. Wait 'til you have them all before you give your recommendations. Then connect their needs with your solutions."

Thaddeus said, "I remember what you taught us about that. Rewind, replay, rekindle, and revalue."

"That's right, replied Andre. "Rewind: go back to what they said earlier. Replay: recount what they said in their own words, or at least pretty close. Rekindle: remind them of why they wanted to accomplish that particular goal. Then revalue: ask them how much they feel it would help their company to make that happen."

"Okay," said Thaddeus. "I think I'm ready."

Andre smiled. "I think so too. Just remember, you'll still get some objections. Work with your decision maker to find a solution. Work within the objection..."

"And never try to *overcome* an objection," said Thaddeus.

Andre nodded. "That's right." He added, "One final reminder. The better your discovery, the fewer their objections. And please keep a list of any objections you do get. We'll discuss them as needed."

Thaddeus laughed and said, "Are you kidding? My discovery's going to be so great, I'll *never* get an objection!"

Andre shook his head and smiled. "Son, you are truly humble, aren't you?"

Thaddeus replied, still laughing, "That's right. I'm awesome at being humble. It's one of my many great character traits!"

Andre grinned. "Let's see how you feel after those presentations."

106

12

Slides and Sticks

T haddeus spent the remainder of the week identifying new prospects and preparing the three touches as part of his "priming the pump" strategy. He was excited to begin contacting companies on Friday morning. He wasn't sure if the greeting cards would've arrived yet, but he just couldn't make himself wait any longer. With each phone call he made, he asked for the decision maker and added, "They should be expecting my call." He carefully tracked the responses from each contact so that he could give Andre feedback on the process.

Just before lunch, Thaddeus walked into Andre's office to update him on the results.

"I called all twenty-five of the companies that I put through the 'priming the pump' process. I spoke with fifteen decision makers. Of the rest, five had their keyholders tell me no, and five were not available for the call."

"How did the conversations go?" asked Andre.

Thaddeus replied, "Of the fifteen I talked with, the overall response seemed very positive. Several mentioned receiving things I'd sent to them. No one seemed to be resistant to my contact. I was able to schedule eight actual meetings. Two said 'thanks,' but they weren't

107

interested. And five said that those decisions will be made near the end of the year—and asked me to contact them again in the October."

Andre said, "You got through to fifteen out of twenty-five decision makers? That's great results! I thought it would go well, but that was much better than I expected."

"Me too!"

Andre asked, "So, what's your plan for keeping in touch with those who'll make decisions later?"

Thaddeus thought for a second, and replied, "I think I'll just keep sending them things. How often do you think I should make the touches?"

"This is new ground for me as well," replied Andre. "I think I'd do it about twice per month, as long as the decision maker sees those contacts as something valuable. Could you tell which of the touches you used this week were getting the best response?"

"Everyone seemed to love the cards," replied Thaddeus. "But they also appreciated the other things. I'll probably mix 'em up a bit just to see if I think one is working better than the others."

Andre said, "Keep me posted. Good work!"

"Thank you. Will do."

As Thaddeus started toward the door, Andre said, "Thaddeus, this is really strong results. But remember, regardless of how good our process is, not everyone's going to say yes. And that's okay. You're just looking for those who do. Do your best work, then allow yourself a certain amount of professional detachment about their response."

"I know, boss. A gallon of no's to find a quart of yeses. I've got this," he said as he waved goodbye.

Thaddeus walked over to his desk and turned off his computer.

I have eleven appointments scheduled with people over the next two weeks. I think I deserve a treat!

Thaddeus knew exactly where he would go for his personal reward—Rosario Boudreaux's.

He parked a couple of blocks away, near where he used to play in the Quarter. As Thaddeus turned the corner, much to his delight, a new Dixieland band he'd never seen before was in full stroll. He stopped and listened. They were playing one of his all-time favorite pieces: *The Saint James Infirmary Blues,* first made famous by the great Louis Armstrong. He closed his eyes and listened to the music.

~ ~ ~

Let her go. Let her go.
God bless her,
Wherever she may be.
She can look this wide world over.
But she'll never find a sweet man like me.

~ ~ ~

The trombonist in the band was also the singer, and he did a great job. His voice even growled—much like Satchmo.

You're good fella, but Louis is still the king.

Thaddeus dropped a five into their tip bucket and began walking. He was looking forward to hearing Livia. This being Friday—a great day for large crowds, he was sure she'd be there.

Since he had extra time, he decided to spend a little of it scouting for businesses in the area.

Maybe it was because he'd just listened to a great band. Maybe it was because he was looking forward to hearing Livia sing. Or maybe it was simply because his mindset was different. But now, he was looking for, and seeing, opportunities and possibilities everywhere. His eyes were opened. His perspective had changed.

He found himself standing in front of a business that he didn't re-member ever seeing before. It was a recording studio, named "Slides and Sticks".

As Thaddeus reached for the door, he said in a quiet voice, "This must be a sign."

A lady was approaching the door, keys in hand. She laughed and said, "It is a sign. It's my sign." She stuck out her hand and said, "I'm Evangeline Chartres. I own the joint. You'll find it easier to get in if I unlock the door first."

Thaddeus shook her hand and replied, "Very nice to meet you Ms. Evangeline. I'm Thaddeus Tucker, and I am so embarrassed that you heard me talking to myself."

She replied, "No. Don't be embarrassed. It's perfectly normal to talk to yourself. It's even perfectly normal to answer yourself. But if you ever say to yourself, 'I'm sorry. Could you please repeat that?'... then you have issues and should immediately seek the help of a qualified medical professional."

Both of them laughed as she unlocked the door and invited Thaddeus inside.

The studio was small. There were large electronic boards, designed for recording dozens of separate tracks. Through the large window that led to the sound studio, Thaddeus could see microphones, headsets, and two comfortable sofas. Along the walls were frames filled with album covers and artist's names.

"So what can I do for you, Thaddeus?"

"Nothing really today," he replied. "I was passing through the area, scouting out some of the local businesses. I'd planned to send a couple of things first, then see about inviting you to visit with me."

"What do you do?"

"I help companies attract and retain exceptional employees through a program we have at Stencil, Osgood, and Broughton."

"Employee benefits?" she asked.

"Yes," he replied.

"I haven't been offering benefits because we're a start-up company, and I only have ten employees. Profit margins are also pretty thin right now."

Remembering his training with Andre, Thaddeus asked, "Are there benefits you've thought about offering before?"

"Yes. I thought about health insurance, and maybe a disability policy."

Thaddeus said, "You mentioned you didn't have many employees, and you had to be mindful of your profit margins. Other than those two things, were there any other reasons that you didn't go ahead?"

"Not really. Those were enough," she said with a laugh.

Thaddeus chuckled for a moment. Then he asked, "With many companies making the tough choice to cut back, or stop benefits all together these days, the idea seems pretty important to you. If you don't think it would be silly for me to ask, why were you considering the idea?"

Evangeline replied, "Not a silly question at all. I'd really like to be able to offer some sort of benefit package. It would help me hire better employees. Plus, I actually like the people on my team and think it would be nice to take care of them in that way."

Wow! If I ask the right questions, and then listen, the decision maker will say exactly what the decision maker needs to hear.

He smiled. "That's the best answer ever. I think I may be able to help in a way that doesn't increase your expenses, and we may even get you a tax break. I can't promise anything yet, but I'm sure we could figure that out in just a few minutes next week. Willing to gamble twenty minutes on me to see if I can help?"

"Absolutely," she said, and they scheduled their meeting.

Twelve! Now I have twelve appointments scheduled!

As Thaddeus was getting ready to leave, he said, "Could I ask you a non-business question? Well, at least not about my business."

"Sure."

"Are you a record label or a recording studio?"

"Both, actually. We have full recording capabilities here. And we also produce and promote artists."

Thaddeus said, "I have a friend who's really great. What do you look for in a singer that makes them worth signing for your label?"

Evangeline looked down and considered the question. Then, with a caring look, returned her eyes to Thaddeus. "I wouldn't want to get your friend's hopes up too much. There are a lot of really talented artists out there who'll never get a contract. Unfortunately, it's not always about talent. I have to look at it from a profitability standpoint. I want them to be great. But I also have to believe that we can both make money by partnering together."

Thaddeus nodded. "That makes sense. After all, it is a business, isn't it?"

"Yes, it is," she replied with a comforting look. "Good luck to your friend, though."

"Thank you. Alright, I'll be on my way. See you next Thursday."

"See you then."

Thaddeus left the recording studio and quickly covered the few blocks to Rosario's. Much to his disappointment, Livia wasn't entertaining her normal crowd on the corner.

That's unusual. I hope everything's okay.

As he walked inside and headed to the bar, he saw Livia walking in from the back of the restaurant.

"There she is!" he said. "I was a little worried when I didn't see you out front. Thought, maybe you weren't coming."

"Are you kidding?" she said as she pulled out the barstool beside Thaddeus and took a seat. "Miss the Friday night crowds? That's not happening."

Thaddeus was glad—and surprised—that she sat next to him. He loved her singing and wanted to be her friend. But with each encounter, she always seemed to hold back just a little. He sensed her hesitancy to just relax and visit with him. He wasn't sure why. Maybe she just made friends slowly. Maybe she was shy. Or maybe she wasn't completely sure of him and his intentions.

Today, however, was different. She seemed comfortable… happy to sit and visit for a few minutes and chat.

"You just getting started?" he asked.

"Yes. I stay later on Friday evenings, so I also start a little later."
She smiled. "How's your week been?"

Thaddeus thought about the last few days.

"It's been really great, actually. Unexpectedly successful. I'm having to learn so many new things, but I feel like I'm getting a handle on it all pretty well. I've had a few successes." He added, "It's been a good week, for sure."

Sensing his excitement, Livia laughed and said, "I can tell."

"How 'bout you?" he asked.

"Not bad. The usual crowds. Everyone's happy and smiling—and videoing."

Livia said, "The other day, you mentioned you were curious how many times those videos are getting watched and shared. You know, I rarely check." She shrugged her shoulders and said, "I think I'm afraid no one's been watching."

Thaddeus said, "It wouldn't surprise me if they were going viral."

She laughed. "Well, it surprised me!"

She said, "I finally did a full search of the hashtag, *#lovingliviain-NOLA.*"

"What'd you find?"

With a bit of a nervous laugh, she replied, "They're getting seen—a lot. I'm not sure how many views a video has to have in order to be considered *going viral…*"

"How many did you see?"

"Over two-hundred-thousand views. It shocked me."

"That's great, Livia! Congratulations! I'm not at all surprised. People love your singing and they love how you interact with them. That's got to be a winning combination."

"Thank you!"

"My pleasure," replied Thaddeus.

He paused for a moment, then said, "You know, I was making a business call at a company a few blocks away. It's a recording studio and a start-up record label…"

Livia interrupted and shook her head. "I haven't had the best of experiences with record labels."

"Well, I met the owner. She seems really nice."

Livia said, "They all do. At least at first."

Thaddeus was excited. "I told her about you and..."

"You what?"

"I told her about you. I told her I have a friend who's really a great singer."

Livia's demeanor completely changed.

Gone was the smile. Gone was her relaxed state of mind. And gone was her friendliness toward Thaddeus.

"Why did you do that?" she asked.

Thaddeus replied, "I was helping. I thought that if the two of you met, she could help you make it to the next level. You know, get you on the big stage."

Thaddeus realized that his efforts, even if well intentioned, were not being appreciated by Livia.

"You were helping?" she asked. "You didn't ask me what I wanted. You didn't ask me if you could help. You didn't ask me one single question. How can you be helpful to me in any way when you don't even know what I want?"

She raised her eyebrows, leaned back in her seat, and said in a low and slow voice, "Do you think you're really that smart? You think you just know what other people need, and then it's okay to take the liberty to do it for them?"

"Well, I..."

"Well, nothing, Thaddeus Tucker. My first experience with record producers was terrible. I don't care to go through that again. I'm not even sure that I'm good enough to make it work."

Thaddeus started to speak. Livia put her index finger up, just a few inches from his face.

"No. Don't speak. Listen. Regardless of your intentions, and even *if* your heart was in the right place, you don't get to do that. The choice is mine. Not yours."

"Livia, I am sorry. I meant no harm."

She got up from the barstool and walked away, muttering something under her breath. Thaddeus couldn't hear what she said, but he knew she wasn't singing his praises. It reminded him of his mother.

She could give Jolie a run for her money.

Thaddeus looked up. Tip was standing there, shaking his head as he wiped a glass with a bar towel. He'd heard the whole conversation.

Thaddeus asked, "Wanna add anything?"

Tip started to reply, then hesitated. He turned to walk away.

After a few steps, he stopped, turned back toward Thaddeus and said, "Bonehead."

Thaddeus had to agree.

After he finished his meal, he walked upstairs and out onto the balcony to listen to Livia as she mesmerized the crowds once again. She never noticed him. Or, at least, she never acknowledged him. He stayed for a few songs and then went back to his car.

His week may have been quite successful. However, it certainly ended on a low note.

What Thaddeus didn't know was that Livia had just taught him a most valuable lesson that he would never forget.

13

Become ObjectionProof™

Monday morning arrived. Thaddeus found himself in the midst of numerous emotions. He was excited. After all, his calendar was full, and he felt good about his chances of opening relationships with several new clients. He was also a little scared. He didn't have much experience yet, and Andre couldn't go with him. So, he had to jump off the boat into the middle of the *sales ocean* and swim—alone.

He was also regretting his last conversation with Livia. Her confidence was far below her value as a performer. People loved her, and her talent was impressive. But she was right. He should've asked first. It was her life.

I had no idea I would upset her so much.

Then he laughed at himself.

I just did what I thought would be helpful. But because I didn't ask... Tip was right. Bonehead! I have to make sure not to make the same mistake with my prospects. Ask first, find out what their needs are, then help them.

Andre had left a note on Thaddeus's desk.

> I have to be out until Wednesday. Good luck with your appointments. We'll talk about them when I return.

> Don't forget to ask great questions in your discovery, and make a list of any objections you get. You've got this!

Thaddeus had three appointments scheduled for Monday, and two for Tuesday. The rest were booked over the following ten days.

As he parked in front of Anderson Manufacturing Company, his first appointment for the day, he pulled out his notes and reviewed his plan. He'd written some key questions on a notepad and planned to have them handy during the meeting. He felt confident, but he knew having those questions easily accessible would be very important should he get a little nervous.

For Thaddeus, getting anxious could cause a case of what seemed like *temporary amnesia*. Being able to look over his questions during the conversation was the best antidote.

The owner of the business stood to shake Thaddeus's hand as he was led into her office.

"You must be Thaddeus," she said. "I'm Jazlyn Anderson. Very pleased to meet you."

"My pleasure. Nice to meet you, Ms. Jazlyn."

Thaddeus smiled. He truly enjoyed the friendly exchange. He remembered Andre saying that people seem to mirror the energy you bring to any meeting. When you're smiling, friendly, and relaxed, people will usually relax, be friendly, and smile in return. When you're tense, unconfident, and apprehensive, they'll sense that as well and be less open to your conversation.

However, the biggest reason for Thaddeus's smile was that on the corner of Jazlyn's desk lay the card he'd sent to her as part of his priming the prospecting pump efforts. On the front cover was a picture of Jazlyn and her family.

Picking it up, she said, "This was a great idea! How in the world did you find this picture?"

Thaddeus replied, "Thank you, ma'am." He added, "I always do some research on the companies that are potential clients for me. As I was looking at your company website, I found that picture. Was that a company picnic?"

"It was. Did you make the card yourself?"

"Actually, I use an online service to send out cards. I pick the picture and create the message. Then the service prints and mails them."

Jazlyn said, "I like that idea so much, I plan to use it too." She winked and said, "And I'll teach my sales team to do the same."

Thaddeus replied, "Ms. Jazlyn, I'd be happy to teach everyone what to do, if you'd like."

"Seriously?"

"Yes, ma'am. It would be my pleasure."

"But I haven't said yes to doing business with you yet."

"That's okay. I do hope you choose to do business with us. But I'll help you with that, either way."

Jazlyn paused, then agreed. "Okay. Thank you."

Thaddeus replied, "My pleasure."

The two visited for a few more minutes, then Thaddeus began his sales conversation.

"In order for us to determine if our companies would work well together, I'll need to ask a few questions. Would that be okay?"

"Absolutely."

Thaddeus said, "As I was doing my research, I saw so many great reviews and accolades for your company. But I never assume that my efforts give me the whole picture. As the owner, what's your favorite thing to brag about with Anderson Manufacturing? What are you the most proud of?"

That great question got the conversation going very well.

Thaddeus worked his way through some additional questions. Jazlyn easily talked through the issues they faced and what she saw as the areas in which they needed improvement. When she had expressed three definite needs—for which Thaddeus felt sure he had some great solutions—he said, "Ms. Jazlyn, I have some good news for you. There are some things you just told me you wanted to accomplish, and our company has some pretty great ways to help you."

Rewind. Replay. Revalue. Rekindle.

"Earlier, you mentioned that you previously wanted to offer disability insurance to your employees, but budgets simply didn't allow you to do so. You said that you really wanted to take care of your team, and it disappointed you when you couldn't."

"Right," replied Jazlyn.

Thaddeus said, "That says so much about you, Ms. Jazlyn. You obviously care about your people. Our company has a disability plan for your employees. It's a plan that you don't have to contribute any company money toward. The premiums are low enough that your employees can comfortably afford the payroll deduction. This gives you the opportunity to protect your profits, take care of your employees in a way that is important to you, and it's a simple process."

Thaddeus asked, "How would you feel about finally being able to do that?"

Jazlyn replied, "I'd like that." She smirked and said, "I'm not saying yes yet. But I like that idea."

Thaddeus laughed. "I understand. No worries."

Then he proceeded to briefly discuss the additional needs she'd expressed in exactly the same manner. When finished, he said, "Why don't I spend a couple of minutes showing you some specifics that I'd recommend in this case. Then, I'll tell you a little about our company, and introduce you to some of our existing clients. I'll let you read what they've said about us."

Once he had wrapped up the details he wanted to share with her, Thaddeus said, "Ms. Jazlyn, I'd like to ask you a question, and please feel completely comfortable telling me no, if that's the right decision for you. Do you see any reason that you wouldn't want to move forward and make our programs available to your employees?"

She thought for a few seconds, smiled and said, "No. I don't think I do. So *now* I'm saying yes," she said with a laugh.

Thaddeus tried his best not to show it, but he was really excited. What an emotional high! He and Jazlyn scheduled the appropriate meetings and completed the authorization.

As he walked out of the building and got back into his car, he yelled, "Yes! Man, I wish Andre was here so I could call him."

Thaddeus had made his first sale. And he'd made it on his first official sales conversation with a decision maker. He felt more confident about his ability to become successful. And he expected his next meetings to go just as well.

They did not.

Although he didn't have decision makers tell him no, they also didn't tell him yes and give him the go ahead. He got objections he didn't know how to handle. But, to his credit, he was streetwise enough to book follow-up meetings with each prospect. He told them he would gather further information, and have some recommendations when they got back together. He made a list of the objections, so that Andre could coach him through the process.

Streetwise to saleswise, he thought. *That's where I'm headed.*

He felt deflated, since no one else moved forward. But he was also excited that Jazlyn had said yes. More importantly, he had confidence that Andre could coach him through the challenges.

He was right.

On Wednesday morning, Andre was already in the break room grabbing a cup of coffee, when Thaddeus walked in.

"Good morning, Thaddeus! Can't wait to hear about your presentations. How'd they go?"

Thaddeus replied, "Great! And then... not so great."

Andre said, "Grab some coffee and let's go talk about it."

As the two men gathered at the conference table in Andre's office, Andre said, "So, walk me through each case. Did you make a list of any objections?"

"Yes, sir. I did."

Thaddeus recounted the story of each sales conversation. He kept notes. He told Andre what the needs were in each case, and what he'd recommended. He also showed a list of objections he'd received.

"One company said yes," he told Andre. It was a textbook example of everything going right. I asked questions. The decision maker talked through the issues and said what she needed to hear. It was perfect. I was ecstatic."

Andre said, "That's great!"

Thaddeus shook his head, and said, "But then the wheels came off. Nobody else said yes. They listened and were polite. It was easy to get them to discuss things with me. I thought I was going to get a similar result. But then they all had objections. Things stalled."

Thaddeus looked down. "It was like a roller coaster. Highest of the highs, one minute. Then lowest of the lows, the next. I kept reminding myself that it's a gallon of nos for a quart of yeses. But I have to admit... it shook my confidence... a little."

Andre's face didn't show disappointment. To the contrary, his face showed that he was, in fact, pleased with Thaddeus.

"First things, first. Thaddeus, don't be disappointed. I'm certainly not. I'm proud of you. You got out there. You did it. And you've started the journey you'll take as you become great at your craft. Also, you landed your first account. That's good stuff!"

Thaddeus perked up a little.

"It's important that you develop the ability to navigate the highs and lows of a sales career. Let me help you reframe this. I want you to see the potential in what you've already accomplished."

Andre asked Thaddeus how many companies he had contacted thus far. Then he asked how many employees work at Anderson Manufacturing. He entered some numbers into his calculator, wrote a dollar amount on his pad, and turned it toward Thaddeus.

"Thaddeus, there's no way to really know what your participation level in the group will be until you complete the enrollment. But, based on our normal averages, you should expect to earn about this much in commission, based only on Anderson. Then, when you divide that dollar amount by the number of companies you've contacted to this date, you've averaged seventy-seven dollars per contact. Whether they said, yes, no, or absolutely nothing, your average is still seventy-seven dollars. When you reframe how you see the process, it makes that emotional roller-coaster level out into a more steady ride."

Thaddeus said, "You're right. That's what you were talking about the other day." He tapped his head. "I don't think it penetrated this hard head until just now."

Andre said, "Some lessons you can learn through education. But others must be learned as you're doing the job."

Thaddeus nodded.

Andre said, "Now, let's discuss the objections you received."

Thaddeus looked at his notes.

"I had one who said our price was too high. One said their employees wouldn't pay for anything. Another said they didn't want to deal with the indirect costs, such as time lost for the employee-benefit meetings, and the time their staff must spend to process the billing. And one, Bosen Automotive Group, said that our competitor is making some pretty big promises that we can't equal."

Andre looked at the list. He said, "I'll give you some things I would say to a decision maker when those objections come up in a minute. But first, I want to give you a framework that will help you."

"Great!"

Andre drew on a piece of paper as he talked.

In large print, he wrote, "*Become ObjectionProof™.*"

Under that, Andre wrote, "**Step one:** Handle common objections during your presentation."

Andre said, "In most industries, ours being no exception, you'll find that there are a few key objections that seem to get expressed on a pretty regular basis. One of the very best ways to neutralize those objections is to discuss them in your actual sales presentation. If your prospect brings the issue up *after* you make your recommendations—it becomes an objection. But if *you* bring up that same issue during your sales conversation, along with the solution to the issue, it transforms into education. That simple process may eliminate their concerns early on."

"What do you mean?" asked Thaddeus. "Can you give me an example?"

"Sure," replied Andre. "For example, if during your recommendation phase, you were to say something like, 'Even though many of our programs can be made available to your employees with no company contributions, you'll still have some indirect costs. Your employees have to be educated on the benefits you'll be making available. Your staff will have to process the bill each month, etc. But with the reduced turnover you'll experience from enhancing your benefit program, along with the payroll-tax savings you'll enjoy from what we do, your return on that minimal investment should easily offset those indirect costs.' Then you can even ask, 'Does that make sense?' and gain their agreement."

Thaddeus said, "That makes sense to me. Hopefully, it will to them as well."

Andre said, "**Step two:** Control your emotions. If *you* overreact, they might too. Stay calm. Stay focused. Then go on to the next step."

"Okay," replied Thaddeus.

Andre continued to write on his notepad.

"**Step three:** Never try to overcome an objection. We talked about that the other day. No one wants someone else to *overcome* them. Instead, work within the objection. Partner with your prospect to find a solution that delivers results for everyone. The great sales trainer Jeff Shore says that we shouldn't overcome or handle objections. Instead, we should neutralize them by working with the prospect to find a solution that makes the issue more palatable. Just like in the indirect cost scenario I just talked about—the issue didn't go away, but we found a solution that's workable."

Thaddeus nodded.

"**Step four:** Empathize with their concern, but stop short of actually agreeing with it."

Thaddeus asked, "How do I do that?"

Andre replied, "Acknowledge that you see their issue as something they should certainly consider. Don't shy away from the issue. But then reframe the objection as something for which you're confident the two of you will find a workable solution. That way, they can still enjoy the benefit of solving the need they discussed with you during your discovery."

"Okay." said Thaddeus.

Andre said, as he wrote, "**Step five:** Dig deeper. The first objection is often not the real objection. It may be a symptom of the real objection. Or it may be a stall—where the prospect knows they're not ready to move forward, but can't exactly put their finger on the reason. So, you'll ask questions to dig a little deeper and help them come up with a solution."

Thaddeus tilted his head slightly and raised his eyebrows.

Andre laughed. "Let me explain. If you were selling a house, and your prospective buyer said that the location was a bit too far from town, you'd first empathize. Then you might ask, 'Do you mind if I ask a couple of questions about that to make sure I understand? What makes it feel like it's too far for you? What are the things you like most about being in town?'"

Thaddeus listened.

"They may mention that since they've always lived close to the city, having the amenities such as shopping, doctors, restaurants, etc., was an important part of their life that they wouldn't want to lose. A potential solution may be for you to show them the development plans for the area, which would bring those same amenities close to their new home. Or possibly, a solution may be that you add up the benefits of getting away from the city and compare that to the extra drive time."

Thaddeus asked, "How would I make that work in our industry?"

Andre considered the question. Then he said, "One of the objections you listed was that our price is too high. After empathizing with them about their concern, you might ask, 'Would you mind if I ask you a couple of questions about that to make sure I understand? When you say the price is too high, are you referring to the actual premium? Or is it more that you don't see the total benefit to the company as being high enough to justify the cost of the premiums?'"

Thaddeus nodded.

Andre said, "Listen to their answers. See where it goes. A potential solution may be to walk them through a discussion where you actually put a dollar value on each benefit they'll receive from the relationship. Easier attraction and hiring of great people for their team… lower employee turnover… plus any payroll-tax breaks they receive can be significant. Think of it like the old-fashioned rocker-balance scales."

Thaddeus said, "I actually have one of those. It belonged to my mother."

Andre added, "My grandma had one too. The decision to buy is often a benefit versus cost analysis—just like on that scale. Keep adding benefits to one side of the equation. When they see *their* benefit as outweighing the cost of implementation, their return on investment will often be enough to help them feel good about moving forward."

Thaddeus said, "I noticed you used that same question in both examples… *Would you mind if I ask you a couple of questions to make sure I understand?* I'm guessing that was no accident."

Andre grinned. "I like how you picked up on that, Thaddeus. Yes. It was on purpose. In my experience, when discussing their objections, I've found that it's best to get their permission first before asking more questions."

"Why's that?" asked Thaddeus.

Andre replied, "Many salespeople want to get right into a question, followed by a debate about the issue. I've found that when you do that, it often puts the decision maker on the defensive."

Thaddeus said, "Like you're trying to overcome the objection, rather than work within it to find a solution."

Andre said, "That's right. But if you ask their permission first, it makes them more comfortable with the process. They correctly see that you're really interested in what they're saying and then finding a solution."

"Fusion point," said Thaddeus.

Andre nodded. "Yes, it is, isn't it?"

After a second, Andre said, "**Step six:** Isolate the issue. Ask them if there are any additional issues or concerns, other than the one you're discussing, which would keep them from moving forward. If there are others, it's best to get them all out on the table prior to offering solutions."

Thaddeus asked, "Would you present the solutions to all issues at one time?"

Andre laughed. "Yes... and no. You'll often find that you only get one objection. But if you get more than one, I'd solve the last one first, and then move up the line if necessary. It's often surprised me that solving their last objection will be enough to move the process forward. And when it's not, be prepared to do the same with the rest."

"Alright," said Thaddeus.

Andre said, "**Step seven:** Solutions, social proof, and close the sale. Offer your solutions, show testimonials from our customers that have addressed the same issue, and ask if they're ready to move forward."

Andre had amassed a binder full of customer testimonial letters. When asking for those testimonials, he'd asked the customers to address specific issues, such as price, employee participation, competition and implementation. Each salesperson could make copies as needed based on the objections they wanted to be prepared for.

Thaddeus had seen the binders. He said, "I love what you've done with customer testimonials."

"Thank you!" said Andre. "Our clients have been great at helping us with that. When you're hoping to set a decision maker at ease on any issue, it's much more effective to have one of our clients—who had the same concern—tell them how well we solved the matter, rather than you telling them how we would accomplish the goal."

"Brilliant!"

Andre asked, "Do you have any more questions?"

"Not really."

"Okay. Why don't you spend some time today looking through the customer testimonial files. Find those who've had the same objections as your prospects."

"Great idea," said Thaddeus, as he got up to leave the room.

Andre said, as he tore the page from his notepad, and handed it to Thaddeus, "Here. Take this with you."

"Thanks, Andre." said Thaddeus.

"My pleasure," replied Andre.

As Thaddeus left the room, he glanced at the page.

Become ObjectionProof

1) Handle common objections during your presentation.

2) Control your emotions.

3) Never try to overcome objections.

4) Empathize with their concerns.

5) Dig a little deeper—is this their real objection?

6) Isolate the objection.

7) Give solutions, social proof, and close the sale.

14

Blind Dates to Long-Term Relationships

T haddeus spent the rest of the morning reviewing testimonial letters. The binders which contained them were well organized. Andre had grouped each customer endorsement, according to the area specifically mentioned within. Thaddeus made copies of those he believed would be the most helpful.

When he got to the section addressing competition, he realized he'd forgotten to ask Andre what he would say to a prospective client who'd received unrealistic promises from another company.

I think I'll see if I can work this out on my own.

He began to read.

On the first page of that section, in large bold letters, Andre had written the following: "Never, under any circumstances, say anything bad about our competition. We have great competitors. We have competitors who aren't so great. But in each case, we will always be respectful and take the high road."

There were many things that Thaddeus liked about Andre. First, Thaddeus respected him. He was a masterful salesperson, and a leader who could transfer that skill set to others. Second, Andre was curious and always open to learning new things.

But the thing Thaddeus loved most about him was simple. Thaddeus believed Andre was indeed a good person. He was kind and helpful. He lived life and did his job in a way that made Thaddeus feel good about working with him—about even knowing him.

As he read the endorsement letters, Thaddeus saw repeated phrases where the clients had stated they "were very happy with the relationship." As a matter of fact, almost every letter in this section mentioned that word—*relationship.*

Thaddeus smiled and looked up. He knew exactly what he would say when he followed up with Bosen Automotive Group. He picked up the phone immediately and called the owner, Ming Jin Bosen.

"Hello, Thaddeus. Do you already have your recommendations ready for me? That was quick!"

Thaddeus laughed, "Yes, sir. I do. But if you'd rather I work a little more slowly, I'll be glad to call you next week."

Ming Jin laughed as well. Thaddeus was relieved. Although he believed that a sense of humor in business was a great way to establish relationships, he'd also come to understand that at times his style of humor may not be the best way to go.

"Do you have a few minutes available this afternoon? I'd like to swing by and give you a brief overview of some things I think you're going to like. I'm going to be in your area around three o'clock. Got fifteen minutes?"

Ming Jin agreed to the meeting time.

Thaddeus walked back over to Andre's office and let him know what he was thinking.

"I like that," said Andre. "Let me know how it goes."

Thaddeus selected twenty-five more potential prospects and began scheduling their first three touches in his "priming the pump" process. He spent a little time in the break room with Lindsay and Lindsey, as they ate their lunch. Then he departed for his afternoon meeting.

Ming Jin Bosen was a kind, energetic, and successful man. His family adopted him and brought him to the United States when he was just a boy. Ming Jin was almost always smiling and made Thaddeus feel he was genuinely glad he'd dropped by to see him—even if he *were* a salesperson.

"Come in, Thaddeus! Welcome! It's so good to see you again," said Ming Jin, as he walked toward Thaddeus.

"Thank you so much, Mr. Bosen."

"Please, call me Ming Jin."

"That's very kind of you. Thank you, Mr. Ming Jin."

The two exchanged pleasantries for a couple of minutes before Thaddeus began to deliver what he'd prepared.

"Mr. Ming Jin, I'm going to share my recommendations with you in just a second. But first, I'd like to thank you. I know that I'm in a competitive situation here, based on what you said on Monday. If I remember correctly, you really liked some things that one of our competitors is discussing with you."

"That's right," said Ming Jin, with a look that let Thaddeus know he was definitely facing an uphill climb.

"Mr. Ming Jin, I look at the sales process pretty much the same as a blind date. Each person is checking the other out to see if there is the possibility for a longterm relationship."

Ming Jin laughed and interrupted. "You're not about to ask me out for dinner, are you?"

Thaddeus laughed too. "No, sir. But I'd gladly treat you to lunch if you'd like to go."

Thaddeus said, "I'm talking about how to start a great relationship that isn't just for the near term. I'm sure you've never had to deal with this before, but I have been on dates that seemed great. But then later, problems popped up."

Ming Jin laughed. "Well, I haven't dated in the last twenty years. I'm happily married. But I get your point."

Thaddeus said, "I finally decided that everyone has their idiosyncrasies and things that are important to them in their day-to-day lives. At least that's true for me. And as a friend of mine says, 'We're all a little crazy. So if we can find someone whose *crazy* matches our *crazy*—well, then they're a keeper.'"

Ming Jin smiled and nodded.

"On first dates, just like in a competitive sales scenario, we all look good, we say the right things, and we present ourselves at our best. But the only way to make sure there is the potential for a great longterm relationship is to be completely up front about who we are and what we can bring to that relationship. We also have to be honest about what we can't."

Thaddeus proceeded to do exactly that. He made his recommendations, telling Ming Jin where he believed Stencil, Osgood, and Broughton excelled and brought great value to their customers. He also told him about areas in which they were working to improve.

Then he said, "There are a couple of things you mentioned you were being offered by our competitor, which I know we simply can't do and remain reasonably profitable. So, even if we agreed to do those things and looked at them as loss-leaders, we'd have to come in later and raise your rates. That's certainly an available business model. It's just not how we choose to do things."

Thaddeus wrapped up the meeting. He said, "I want our company to be a great *first date* with yours. But more importantly, I want to put you and your company, along with me and my company, in a position that two years from now you realize it wasn't just a great first date. It was the beginning of a very profitable relationship for you, and one of the best business decisions you've ever made in this area."

Thaddeus then pulled out a copy of a testimonial letter from a client who had been with Stencil, Osgood, and Broughton for five years. The letter detailed how they had switched to them after being with another reputable company, and five years later, they were still very happy that they'd made that switch.

Thaddeus moved the letter over to Ming Jin. "This company has told us we're welcome to have potential clients call them for a reference. So, if that is something that you'd like to do, it's perfectly okay."

Ming Jin read the letter. Then he looked up at Thaddeus and said, "Thank you, Thaddeus. You've certainly given me some things to consider. I'll do that and get back to you in a few days."

"Thank you so much for your time, Mr. Ming Jin."

Ming Jin said, "My pleasure. We'll talk soon."

Thaddeus left the meeting with a sense that it had gone well. But he wasn't sure what the results would be. Either way, he believed he'd done his best.

He headed over to Rosario Boudreaux's to see if Livia was singing. He owed her an apology, and he didn't want to delay. His dad often said, "When it comes to apologies—or going to the dentist—it's better to do it sooner rather than later."

His dad was right.

Before reaching the corner, Thaddeus could hear Livia singing. Rounding the turn, he saw a considerable crowd enjoying her performance. The faces may have changed, but their actions remained the same. They loved Livia, and she loved them. It didn't seem to matter what day of the week it was. Livia always drew the people in, and it was a magical experience for everyone.

Thaddeus remained in the background until she finished her set. Then he walked up and sat down beside her.

"Do you have a minute?"

She nodded. She was quiet and reserved. Cautious.

"Livia, I owe you an apology. I acted in a way that was inappropriate. I thought I was doing a good thing… what I thought you needed. But, I didn't ask. I just acted."

Thinking of the lessons he was learning in his sales career, he said, "I've long had the habit of telling people what they should do and how they should do it… pretty much my whole life. But unfortunately, I've not had the habit of asking questions and listening. I'm learning to do that now. But I totally failed to do that with you. I consider you a friend, and I'm sorry."

He finished, "Would you want to forgive me? Please?"

Livia leaned back, relaxed, and smiled.

"Yes, Thaddeus. I'll forgive you." Then she added, "If you'll forgive me too."

"What do you mean?"

She said, "Thaddeus, you should've asked me what I wanted first. That's true. But your heart was in the right place. I overreacted. The simple truth is that I'm not very confident about my singing career. The feelings that insecurity generates inside of me are no fun at all. That day, I reacted from those feelings more than from what you did."

She asked, "So, will you forgive me as well?"

"Of course."

She added, "And thank you for trying to help me. I appreciate it."

Thaddeus replied, "My pleasure."

Livia stood to pack her gear and go into Rosario's.

"Are you going inside?" she asked.

Thaddeus replied, "Not today. I just came to apologize to you."

Livia asked, "You came all the way over here just to say you're sorry?"

"Yes, I did."

"Thank you," she said as she walked away.

She turned back.

"Thaddeus?"

"Yes, ma'am?"

She thought about what she was going to say.

With the slightest nod, she said, "If you want to mention me to anyone, including that record producer, you have my permission. It's okay with me."

Thaddeus didn't reply. He just sighed, with a warm sense of relief, as she walked into the restaurant.

15

Education vs. Objection

The next week, Thaddeus continued feeding new names into his sales pipeline, priming the prospecting pump, making new contacts, sending out touches, and having sales conversations with decision makers. His confidence and his skills were growing with each day. He was still learning. But he was getting the feeling that accepting this sales position was going to be one of his better decisions.

On Thursday morning, he arrived for his 11:30 AM meeting with Evangeline Chartres, the owner of Slides and Sticks, a few minutes early. As he waited outside, an idea came to mind. He picked up his phone and dialed the number for Rosario Boudreaux's.

A male voice answered the line.

"Rosario Boudreaux's. This is Tip. How may I help you?"

Surprised, Thaddeus asked, "Tip? What are you doing answering the phone? Are you a host now? This is Thaddeus Tucker."

"Hi Thaddeus. No. I was just walking by the phone and picked it up."

"Tip, there is obviously no end to your skill set!" he said with a laugh. "I have a quick question."

"Shoot."

"Do you know if Livia will be singing today?"

"She will be. In fact, she's already out there. Why?"

"No reason. I was thinking about coming over for lunch, and I wanted to check."

"Well, you did. She is. And I'm glad we got that settled. Need anything else?"

"No. I'm good. See you soon."

At 11:25, Thaddeus walked in the door. Evangeline was standing in the lobby and greeted him.

"Hello, Thaddeus."

"Good morning, Ms. Evangeline. How are you doing?"

She replied, "If I were doing any better, the government would pass a tax on me for being too happy!"

Thaddeus laughed. "They're gonna to do it anyway, so you may as well just enjoy yourself!"

The two walked into Evangeline's office, and Thaddeus started the sales conversation. Everything went well. He'd planned ahead and worked several of the common objections into his presentation.

If they voice the issue after the fact, it's an objection. If I bring it up during my presentation—along with the solution—it's education.

After, Thaddeus made his recommendations and asked if Evangeline was ready to move forward.

"I am," she said, with a smile.

Changing the subject, Thaddeus asked, "Would you mind if I ask you some questions on a different subject—again?"

She nodded.

"The other day, you mentioned that it's very tough for a new artist to get a record contract. What you said certainly made sense to me. But it got me thinking. Do you mind sharing with me what you look for in an artist? What makes them a profitable risk for you?"

She considered his question.

"Are you talking about your friend?"

Thaddeus replied, "Yes. But not just her. I'm always out and meeting new people. I love music." He paused. "I guess what I'm asking you is what do I need to be looking for out there to know if someone would be a great referral for me to send your way?"

Evangeline paused to think, then answered.

"That's a great question, and I appreciate the help. We are a new label, and finding new talent—the right new talent—is an arduous task. Yet it's obviously necessary."

She said, "I'll invest a lot of money up front. If the act is really great and the recordings sell well, I'll recoup my investment. Then, if it continues to earn, there will be royalties for both our company and the artist. If the sales don't come, I lose a significant investment."

Thaddeus nodded.

Evangeline said, "So I look for three things, primarily. First, they have to be great. If their talent isn't among the best, I don't take the chance. But the truth is, talent is just the small first step. It gets their hand on the door, but doesn't open it."

She added, "Next comes work ethic. Nothing happens without it. An artist is like an author in this case. My company will produce the product and help market it to a certain extent. But if the artist doesn't work very hard to promote themselves, I won't work with them. Sales don't just magically happen. It takes a commitment to build a following of listeners."

Thaddeus asked, "And number three?"

"Third is that they must have a following already. If they're performing in clubs, I want to see that their performances are well attended and the crowds love them. I want to see that they have a social-media following too. You'd be surprised at how much that helps when you're trying to get a new artist off the ground."

Thaddeus nodded and smiled. *Yes, indeed,* he thought.

"Well thanks for telling me what to look for. I'll keep my eyes open and try to help."

Evangeline said, "Thank you, Thaddeus. That's very thoughtful."

As he stood to leave, he said, "I'm headed over to my favorite restaurant to have lunch. Would you like to join me? My treat!"

137

She replied, "That sounds nice. Where are we going?"

"Rosario Boudreaux's."

"Great! I've been meaning to try that place. Just haven't had the time. I'll lock up here and meet you there in fifteen minutes."

As Thaddeus walked to Rosario's, he couldn't help but be excited. He'd just made another sale. His future was on an upward track. And he was looking forward to having Evangeline hear Livia.

When Evangeline arrived, Thaddeus asked the host if she would seat them on the upper balcony so they could enjoy the day. They ordered their meals. Their drinks were delivered just as Livia started to entertain the crowd.

Looking at the crowd, Evangeline said, "That's a good crowd for a busker on a Thursday."

"Is that right?" he asked. "Every time I've seen her here, she draws a crowd at least that big."

Evangeline said, "And her voice is *really* unique. It's kind of a cross between the old jazz masters, with a little bit of other cultures thrown in as well." She closed her eyes. "I'm hearing a little hip-hop… maybe a little reggae? I like it."

Thaddeus asked, "Do you see all of those people with their phones out recording her?"

"I do. And that's great. But the real question is, are they sharing what they're seeing?"

Thaddeus pulled out his phone and searched the Internet for the hashtag, *#lovingliviainNOLA*. He turned the phone around and placed it in front of Evangeline.

She looked at the screen and scrolled through the pages. "That is a *very* large following. She's getting hundreds of thousands of views. That's really…" she paused. "Wait, a minute. Is that your friend?"

"Yes, ma'am. It is. I promise I didn't bring you here under false pretenses. I wanted to take you to lunch as a thank you for becoming my client. But after you mentioned the things you look for in a new artist… well, I thought this may be the perfect place to bring you."

She looked at Thaddeus then turned toward Livia and listened.

Thaddeus said, "Why don't we just sit here and enjoy her for a while? You can see how she works with the crowd. Then, and only if you'd like for me to, I'll introduce you."

Evangeline asked, "What's in this for you?"

Thaddeus chuckled a little. "Nothing. I'm helping introduce two of my friends to each other because they may be able to do business together. No agenda. Just something I like to do."

After about thirty more minutes, Evangeline suddenly stood up and started walking away. The abruptness startled Thaddeus, and he didn't know what to do.

She turned back toward him, smiled and tilted her head. "You coming?"

He laughed and said, "Yes, ma'am. Just as soon as I pay the check."

When they arrived at the corner, Livia was just finishing her set. She smiled at Thaddeus.

"Hi, Livia. This is Evangeline Chartres. She owns Slides and Sticks, a recording studio and record label a couple of blocks from here. Ms. Evangeline, this is my friend, Livia Cole. She's a hard worker. She entertains the crowds better than any busker I've ever known. And she may be the most gifted singer I've had the opportunity to enjoy."

He continued, "Livia, Evangeline occasionally works with new artists. I know her. I like her. And even though I've known her for only a short while, I trust her."

He took Livia by the hand, and said, "I think you can too."

The two ladies exchanged hellos.

Thaddeus said, "I think I'll leave now and, if you two are so inclined, you can take it from here."

As he turned to walk away, Livia said, "Hey, Thaddeus."

He turned back.

With a smile that melted Thaddeus's heart, she said, "Thank you, my friend."

16

Sing a New Song

What a year!

Just twelve months ago, Thaddeus had wisecracked his way into getting fired, then gotten forgiven, and entered into a sales career for which he had not been prepared. He thought back about that day last year, sitting in the Louis Armstrong Park, remembering the sound of his mother's voice. He wasn't so sure that she would have been proud of his actions that day. But he had absolutely no doubt that she would be proud of him now.

I wish you were here to see this, Mom.

Over the year, he had become proficient in his sales skills. He was comfortable with what he was doing. The entire process took time, but without a doubt, he knew he could do the job now. He was happy. He was making more money than he'd ever made before. And Andre had even mentioned the idea that he should consider a promotion into a leadership position.

"Thaddeus, you're really good at sales now. Not because of your natural talent. You're exceptional because you've learned what to do, and then applied what you've learned very well."

Then Andre said, "It's my experience that the best sales managers are usually those who struggled at first. They had to work hard to master their skills. And since they had to learn from scratch—they are often great teachers."

Thaddeus wasn't in a hurry to get into sales management. But he was considering the idea. He knew it would be more work. But it would also mean more income, and he thought he would enjoy the job.

But tonight was not a work night. He was attending a concert at the civic center.

The civic center was an older New Orleans venue, with ornate wood carvings on the walls throughout, and was considered a cultural masterpiece. If his father had been by his side, Thaddeus was sure he would hear tales of how the building was first built in the early 1900s, was left in disarray, and then revitalized into one of the most prominent concert venues in the South. The smell of history and old wood filled the air. There were hundreds of seats on the first level, and two rear balconies. Along the sides of the hall were two smaller balconies with box seats.

The 1,200 seat auditorium was filled to capacity.

Although he'd attended concerts at the civic center before, this was the first time an attendant had ever guided him to the wings offstage. There, Thaddeus joined Evangeline. She said nothing. She just smiled and gave him a hug.

Thaddeus had a special backstage pass. And he was listening to a very special friend as she sang.

Even though she was entertaining a much larger crowd of people, Livia still cradled each of their hearts in her hands with a magnetism few entertainers really seemed to understand.

But Livia was a master.

"For my next song, I'm going to sing an original for you. I first wrote this song when I was just getting started busking on the streets of New Orleans. I wasn't very sure of myself. But I knew I loved to sing. I hope you enjoy it."

The musicians began to play, and Livia's voice filled the room. Slow. Heartfelt. Warm and simply lush.

~ ~ ~*Livia's Song*~ ~ ~

Sittin' in the heart of my dreams.
Wrapped in the ghosts of music all around.
The chords are rich, the melodies seem
Filled with the soul I've found.

~

Eyes that only see me smile.
Ears that only hear the music in the air.
Hands that clap, swaying with style
Dance the street without care.

~

I wonder if they'd stay,
Or go along their way,
If they could see inside,
This fear I try to hide,
They tell me that I'm more
Than I've ever been before.
"I just need to believe."

~

Believe in me?
Seems like an easy thing.
Just make the choice.
Then rejoice.
Shine your star for all to see.

~

Believe in me?
But I see all my flaws.
Can I make the choice?
Overcome the little voice
That whispers "There's no 'believe' in me."

~ ~ ~

The musicians continued to play, and Livia again talked with the crowd.

143

"I love that song. I really do. It brings back so many memories for me that just fill me up, ya know?"

The crowd hung on her words, absorbed in the experience.

"But, so many great things have happened over the last year—I decided to write a different ending. I'd like to debut the new lyrics with you tonight, if that'd be alright. Would that be okay with you guys?" she asked. The crowd applauded and gave her encouragement.

"But I'd like to bring a friend of mine out here with me too, if y'all don't mind." The crowd again cheered and applauded. Livia turned toward the side, to Thaddeus, and motioned for him to join her on stage.

Thaddeus wasn't comfortable being onstage in front of a big crowd like this. But he would never let his friend down. So, he stepped out onto the stage. A little awkward. A little slow. But he walked to the center and took Livia's extended hand. He saw her parents in the front row. He'd met them at Rosario Boudreaux's once, around Christmas, and really enjoyed them.

She said, "Thaddeus, I wouldn't be here tonight if it weren't for you. You're a good friend. Thank you."

Thaddeus tried to hold back the tears. It didn't work. He hoped the crowd couldn't see, but he knew Livia could.

She began to sing again.

~ ~ ~Livia's New Song~ ~ ~

Sittin' in the heart of my dreams.
Wrapped in the ghosts of music all around.
The chords are rich, the melodies seem
Filled with the soul I've found.

~

Eyes that only see me smile.
Ears that only hear the music in the air.
Hands that clap, swaying with style

Dance the street without care.

~

I wonder if they'd stay,
Or go along their way,
If they could see inside,
This fear I try to hide,
They tell me that I'm more
Than I've ever been before.
"I just need to believe."

She spoke to the crowd as the musicians continued to play. She giggled. "This is the new part." The way she said it was like a shy little girl. So sweet.

Believe in me?
Seems like an easy thing.
Just make the choice.
Then rejoice.
Shine your star for all to see.

~

Believe in me.
My friend, you showed me the way.
I made the choice
Now that inner-voice
Says "There is 'believe' in me."

~ ~ ~

She pulled Thaddeus closer, gave him a kiss on the cheek, and said, "Thaddeus, thank you. Now I believe in me, too."

~ ~

THE END

Take Away Summary

Generate Fusion Points™ in Your Prospecting

- Prime Your Prospecting Pump:

  Generate three positive emotional contacts with your prospect prior to inviting them to your first meeting.

- Focus on *their* benefit from *your* proposition:

  Use phrases, with each person in your sales model, that direct their attention to how they personally benefit from doing what you're asking them to do.

- Extend an invitation:

  Instead of asking for a meeting, invite your prospect to visit with you to explore whether *their* benefit from *your* proposition may work in their specific situation—with no obligation on their part.

How to Close a Decision Influencer

- If possible, include the final decision maker in your meeting. But when that is not a possibility, treat the decision influencer with the same respect as if they were the one-and-only person who can give you permission to move forward.

- Take them off the hook:

  I'd like to ask you a question, and please feel completely comfortable and welcome to tell me no, if that's the right answer for you. Fair enough?

- Give them a promotion:

  Use a lighthearted phrase to mentally place them in the mindset of the final decision maker.

- Ask your closing question:

  If the final decision were yours, and yours alone, do you see any reason you wouldn't want to move forward with my recommendations?

- Go to work for them:

  If they have objections, work within those objections to find a solution. If they say that they would move forward with you, go to work for them. Offer your services to have the conversation with the decision maker (or makers) to make things easier for them. Get that meeting on their calendar.

Become ObjectionProof™

- Become GREAT at discovery:

  The better *your* discovery—the fewer *their* objections. Ask great questions which result in your prospect hearing their specific needs, coming from their mouth—not yours. Ask questions that direct them toward *their* value from *your* proposition.

- Education versus objection:

Bring up common objections—along with their solutions, during your sales conversations. When you bring up an issue in your presentation, followed by the solution, it's education. When your prospect brings it up after your presentation, it's an objection.

- Never try to overcome an objection:

Work within the objection, together with your prospect, to find a solution that provides a win-win scenario.

Then Set the Frame

- Keep your emotions under control.

Your prospect will often respond based on the emotional cues they pick up from you. Stay focused and calm.

- Empathize with their concern:

Acknowledge that their concern is a valid consideration, but stop short of agreeing.

- Dig deeper:

Ask questions to find out if their objection is the real issue—or is it simply a surface-level symptom of another underlying concern.

- Isolate the issue:

Ask if there are any other concerns that would keep them from moving forward.

- Provide solutions:

Recommend solutions. Give social proof—testimonials from your clients who either had (or expected to have) the same issues. Then close the sale.

A Special Message from the Authors

We've truly loved bringing you, *Streetwise to Saleswise: Become ObjectionProof™ and Beat the Sales Blues.* Our goal is for you to have found the story engaging, the principles empowering, and the book now helpful in increasing your sales and leadership success.

If we've accomplished that endeavor, and you feel you've received tremendous value from the book, we'd like to ask you a special question. Of course, there's absolutely no obligation on your part.

Would you like to help us spread the word?

A meaningful book can have a lasting impact when it becomes a dynamic movement through word of mouth.

So how can you help? With your permission, we'd like to suggest any or all of the following:

- Post a brief review on Amazon, or your favorite book retailer's website. A few sentences will help others to find the book.
- Take a quick picture of yourself holding the book and share your thoughts on social media. Be sure to tag us.
- Share the book with sales professionals and sales managers within your company or your sphere of influence.

We are HUGELY grateful for your kindness!

Thanks so much,

— Jeff and Bob

About the Authors

Jeff C. West is the bestselling and award-winning author of the heartwarming sales fables, *The Unexpected Tour Guide*, winner of the Axiom Business Books Bronze Medal, and co-author (with Lisa M. Wilber) of *Said the Lady with the Blue Hair,* winner of the Axiom Business Books Silver Medal and a finalist with both the National Indie Excellence and the American Book Fest Awards. He has been a guest on numerous national and international sales and leadership programs such as *The Go-Giver Podcast with Bob Burg, The Go-Giver Community's Conversations with Legends, The Buyer's Mind with Jeff Shore, The Author Your Brand Show with Doug Crowe, The Business Growth Advantage with Joey C. Vitale* and many more.

With over thirty years of successful sales and sales leadership experience, including 21 years with the *Fortune 500®* insurance company Aflac, Jeff is a sought-after speaker in multiple industries and his client list includes companies such as Aflac, Edward Jones, Link Staffing, and others.

Connect with Jeff at: www.jeffcwest.com

Free Sales Training Series: www.survivalskillsforcommission-salespeople.com

 **Bob Burg** is a Hall of Fame speaker and author of numerous books including *Endless Referrals,* and co-author (with John David Mann) of the international bestseller, *The Go-Giver*, which has sold over 1 million copies and been translated into 32 languages.

The Go-Giver was rated #10 on *Inc.* magazine's list of the "Most Motivational Books Ever Written" and was on *HubSpot's* 20 "Most Highly Rated Sales Books of All Time."

Throughout his 35-year career he has helped large companies, small business entrepreneurs, and the many in-between, to more effectively communicate their value, sell at higher prices with less resistance, and grow their businesses based on his Endless Referrals system.

Bob is an advocate, supporter, and defender of the free enterprise system, believing that the amount of money one makes is directly proportional to how many people they serve.

He is also an unapologetic animal fanatic.

Connect with Bob at: www.Burg.com

Subscribe to Bob's free Daily Impact email: www.burg.com/daily-impact

A Free Gift For You

Bob and Jeff would like to share a free 3-part
video series with you based on the principles
found in *Streetwise to Saleswise.*

*How to Master the Art of Becoming
ObjectionProof™*

*To get your free gift, please go to
https://jeffcwest.com/videos/*

Or scan this QR Code.

Made in United States
North Haven, CT
28 February 2024